The National Literacy Trust

Guide to Books on Literacy Published during 1996

Edited by

Nigel Hall

Published by The National Literacy Trust
1997

ISBN 1 900 904 01 2

The National Literacy Trust
Swire House,
59 Buckingham Gate
London SW1E 6AJ

Tel: 0171 828 2435
Fax: 0171 931 9986
Email: contact@literacytrust.org.uk

Contents

Editorial

We have made it to a second year. Once again, I need to thank all those publishers who have sent books for inclusion in the Guide, and all those contributors listed below who have spent time composing the descriptions.

Despite the title of the guide referring only to books published in 1996, I have started a policy of including books from the previous year which escaped our attention in time for last year's Guide. There are many reasons why such books are overlooked: some we simply never heard about; some are published so late in the year that by the time they reach us we are into the next year; and some simply because publishers did not send them. Because this Guide is a resource for those interested in books about literacy, we felt that to ignore missed titles would make the Guide less useful than it should be. Thus, from now on, Guides will include not only the books published in the year indicated in the title of the Guide, but will also include overlooked books published during the previous year. We do not normally intend to go back any further than one year.

Reaction to last year's guide has been good, although we still appear to have some difficulty in persuading a few publishers that we are suitable place to send their books. To our dismay there are several literacy book publishers who have not responded to any letters. One wonders how serious they are about bringing knowledge of their books to a wider audience. In a few cases it is clear that a publisher has had trouble understanding what might count as a book on literacy and a dialogue with one such publisher has led me to think more deeply about the nature of this guide, and in particular, what counts as a book about literacy.

Literacy is an inherently ambiguous term. Along one dimension, it could include any printed or written text; after all, they all represent the consequences of literate behaviour. Along another dimension we could follow some contemporary writers about literacies and accept almost any subject. So mathematical literacy, scientific literacy etc. could legitimately find a place. Along another dimension lies the whole field of literature. Clearly, it would be ridiculous for this

1

Guide (as well as detrimental to the health of the editor) to take the notion of literacy in its widest senses and try and capture everything along all the possible dimensions. So what does count, in the terms of this Guide, as a book about literacy?

In a letter to a doubting publisher, I described a book about literacy as being one which raises issues about the nature, function and effects of literacy. To this I would want to add 'the learning and teaching of literacy'. While this narrows the field down, it nevertheless creates many grey areas, for such descriptions could pertain to books which conventionally have their roots in other distinct disciplines. Where exactly is the boundary between a book which is about literature, and a book about literature which in the process of being so, raises issues about the nature, function and effects of literacy? There are a number of such examples in the first section of this year's guide.

Clearly books about Henry James's style, or the internal stylistics of Shakespearian poetry are not books about literacy in the terms of this Guide. But once a book which starts as a literary study raises significant issues about the nature, function and effects of literacy, then it becomes an appropriate book for this Guide. Having tried to explain that to the literature editor of a major British publisher, she responded, "but isn't your guide mainly about teaching literacy?"

It does not take much more than a quick look to see that a considerable portion of this book does indeed feature texts relating to teaching and learning literacy in and out of educational settings. However, that proportion is a measure of the size of the literacy education market, not a measure of what this Guide is trying to do, and in this and the previous guide, I have put first, significant sections about books whose topics lie outside the educational world.

I happened recently to be standing outside Foyles in London. It is sometimes described as the largest bookshop in the world, but I have stood outside a number of bookshops about which that claim has been made. Nevertheless, it is pretty big. I wondered how I would get on if I went in wanting to look at books on literacy as I have defined it above. Where would I start? That is where this book comes in. It assumes that there is a relationship between all the books featured in it which warrants their gathering together under one conceptual heading. I do not assume that everyone is interested in every book about literacy, but I do assume that many interested in literacy have concerns which go beyond just one domain within literacy, and I do assume that in many instances domains are interrelated.

In my life beyond editing this guide, I am a specialist in the literacy education of young children. There are plenty of books wholly about the literacy education of young children, but I have found in recent years that in asking questions about my topic I have been led to read sociological, anthropological, linguistic and historical texts on literacy. In fact, the books which have contributed most to changes in my thinking on my subject have often come from outside the world of education. That may be a good or a bad thing depending upon one's view of what it is I do. However, from my perspective, this broader contextualisation has been refreshing, has opened up new ways of thinking and has made significant differences to what I write, think about, and teach where literacy is concerned. Hopefully this guide will not simply inform those with a specialist interest but will enable many readers to see that books in other areas may have something to offer their interest.

The entries are all arranged in a particular order. First comes the author's name, followed by the full title. Then comes the number of pages, place of publication and publisher. Where a book is published in more than one country it is, where known, the originating publisher that comes first. Then follows the hardback ISBN number and price, and then the paperback ISBN number and price (unless there is no hardback edition). If the book is published in a second country, as many are, then follows the details for those countries.

It is worth bearing in mind two points. The first is that many new books take a while to appear in another country and often do so under a different imprint. If a book is marked as not available in your country, or that there was no information available, it is still worth checking. Changes occur all the time. The second point relates to prices. We have included prices in the UK as of

December 1996, and in the US as of October 1996 (which was the latest price guide to which, at the time of publication, we had access). We suggest you always check with your bookseller for the up-to-date price of any book.

We hope you find this booklet useful. If you are a publisher, please send us any relevant titles for the 1997 guide. If you are an author, make sure your latest book reaches us. And, if you know of books published during 1996 which have not been noticed in this guide, let us know, as we will be pleased to include them in next year's guide.

From next year, the guide will be edited by a group from the Education Department at Sheffield University. If you have suggestions for the guide, or books that you would like to send for inclusion, please send them to:

Dr. Jo Weinberger
The University of Sheffield
Division of Education
The Education Building
388 Glossop Road
Sheffield S10 2JA

The entries in this year's guide have been written by: Waltraud Boxall, Katinka Bryan, Janet Evans, Julia Gillen, Rob Greenall, Nigel Hall, Cathy Nutbrown, Kate Pahl, John Rainer, Jean Robertson, Anne Robinson, Yvonne Sinclair, Liz Thomas, Chris Turner, and Jo Weinberger

Any views contained within the book descriptions are those of the compilers and are not necessarily those of The National Literacy Trust.

Non-educational books about literacy

Atkinson, Paul., Davies, Brian and Delamont, Sarah
*Discourse And Reproduction: Essays In Honor Of Basil
Bernstein* 297p. New Jersey: Hampton Press. ISBN Hb.
1881303047 $65.00; **Pb.** 1881303055 $26.50. Distributed
in the UK by Eurospan, Hb. £51.95, Pb. £21.50. (1995)
Basil Bernstein has been one of the most influential British
sociolinguists during the last forty years and continues to be so (as
demonstrated in the emergence of the Australian genre theorists and
the recent changes in British educational practice towards more
visible pedagogy in schools). This volume of essays marks his
retirement, and within it a range of authors, from many countries,
write not about Bernstein but on ideas that derived from issues
originally raised by him. The fourteen chapters between them deal
with many aspects of Bernstein's work, and perhaps importantly
for general readers most authors locate these in contemporary
concerns. While much of Bernstein's early work was directed
towards oral language, in general his theories have powerful
implications for all pedagogic practice. Thus while this book has
only a limited amount of writing directly related to literacy, in other
respects most of the chapters have important messages for those
engaged in literacy education.

Beetham, Margaret *A Magazine Of Her Own: Domesticity
And Desire In The Woman's Magazine 1800-1914* 242p.
London: Routledge. ISBN Hb. 0415049201 £45.00. ISBN Pb.
0415141125 £14.99. In the USA, Hb. $59.95 and Pb. $17.95
This book explores how the woman's magazine became established
as a popular and influential medium during the nineteenth century.
This very thorough yet readable book traces the history of the
women's magazine and how it served to define and redefine the
women that constituted its principal readership. A substantial
amount of the book is given over to case studies of magazines
including Beeton's English Women's Domestic Magazine and The
Queen. Beetham discusses how women's magazines exist in a
dynamic relationship with the discourses of their time, thus the
evolving nature of these serials was both 'caught up in the social
formations and power inequalities of gender, class and nationality'

and yet at the same time had the capability of challenging these forces.

Behar, Ruth and Gordon, Deborah (Eds.) *Women Writing Culture* 457p. California: University of California Press. ISBN Hb. 0520202074 $48.00. ISBN Pb. 0520202082 £16.95. In the UK, Hb. £38.00 and Pb. 13.95. (1995)
The book is concerned with questions relating to feminism, writing and anthropology. There is one chapter which is of interest to adult literacy practitioners on the process of teaching 'critical literacy' and how this empowers students, based on an adult literacy project in New York. It examines the role literacy plays in gender identity and citizenship. Other chapters look at writing, narrative, gender and class in a feminist anthropological framework. The book explores and re-defines notions of literacy in minority discourses and offers new readings of a wide range of texts from Chinese Americans, Israeli poets, African Americans and Egyptian Bedouins, with a flexible and questioning approach taken to the primacy of literate cultures.

Bergeron, David (Ed.) *Reading And Writing In Shakespeare* 289p. Newark: Delaware University Press. ISBN Hb. 0874135575 $42.50. Published in the UK by Associated University Presses, £32.50.
As an author Shakespeare wrote in a time of dynamic tension between the oral and the written. Within his writing the notion and act of reading and writing are highly visible phenomenon and the essays in this book (deriving from contribution to a seminar on the topic) explore various ways in which Shakespeare's use of writing reflected wider cultural changes in concepts about literacy; these include: the position of readers responding to texts; questions of authorship and authority; and questions of interpretation. The essays include: one which suggests how particular systems of punctuation are related to ways in which writing describes character; an examination of Lady Macbeth's acts of reading and writing; an investigation into the relationship between martyrdom and writing; and an analysis of writing, history and power. This is an unusual book but one which raises a host of interesting questions about reading and writing in the seventeenth century.

Berniger, Virginia *Reading And Writing Acquisition: A Developmental And Neuropsychological Perspective* 223p. Boulder, Colorado: Westview Press. ISBN Pb.0813330009 $18.95. In the UK, £12.95.

This book is divided into two main sections. The first outlines the theoretical foundations which underpin and define the developmental neuropsychological perspective with relation to reading and writing acquisition. The second section explores a wide range of previous research conducted in psychology, biology, education and cognition. The book provides a theoretical framework for the integration of biological and educational perspectives in explaining differing levels of achievement in the development of reading and writing. It also addresses the communication gap between theory-driven research on learning processes and the practical considerations involved in accessing, preventing and remediating reading and writing difficulties and disabilities. The readership for this book includes undergraduate and graduate students of psychology, particularly those interested in developmental psychology or literacy. Practitioners in the field of child clinical psychology and educational psychology may also find the book valuable.

Birkerts, Sven *The Gutenberg Elegies: The Fate Of Reading In An Electronic Age* 231p. London: Faber. ISBN 0571190456 £7.99. In the USA, Hb. published by Faber, ISBN 057119849, $22.95. Pb. published by Fawcett, 0449910091, $12.50.

Birkerts' book (originally published in the USA in 1994 but now published in the UK) derives from the author's interest in the ways in which technological change are impacting on conventional notions of reading. The book has two major sections. The first is what Birkert describes as a subjective ecology of reading, a stance which he honestly characterises as a kind of 'Luddite' position. The second major section explores how a variety of forces are threatening the primacy of book reading as a central language activity. The chapters are individual essays and therefore do not constitute a developing argument but rather one which gathers force incrementally. The book is highly polemical but perhaps in times when new technologies are being embraced as if they are manna from heaven, it is useful to have a text which reminds us of the power of the good old book.

Cartmell, Deborah., Hunter, I., Kaye, H. and Wheelan, I.
*Pulping Fiction: Consuming Authors Across The
Literature/Media Divide* 160p. London: Pluto Press. ISBN
Hb. 0745310710 £35.00. **Pb.** 0745310702 £10.99. In US, **Pb.**
$15.95.
This book is Volume One in a series called Film/Fiction, which
addresses the developing interface between English and Media
studies. This volume focuses principally on interpretations of
classic literature for film and television, although there are chapters
on specific film effects and techniques. This volume sets out to
examine some of the consequential tensions inherent in developing
analytical techniques for identifying worthwhile and illuminating
examples of mass culture. Contributors to the volume are always
mindful of a contemporary context where texts are less easily
categorised as canonical or non-canonical. An opening chapter
establishes in a scholarly fashion a theoretical and analytical
framework for investigating adaptations, paying due attention to
their special visual features. Subsequent chapters explore particular
features of specific adaptations, ranging from Shakespeare, through
Middlemarch, to Pulp Fiction.

Castle, Kathryn *Britannia's Children: Reading
Colonialism Through Children's Books And Magazines*
198p. Manchester: Manchester University Press. ISBN Hb.
0719028531 £40.00.
The author takes as her premise that there were strong links
between education, the juvenile press and imperial propagandists,
and that there was the intention and the opportunity to transmit
the imperial message to the young. Castle examines and focuses
upon the characterisation, identity and histories attributed to the
imperial subjects of Africa, China and India. The three different
subjects are examined in turn with some attention being paid to the
particular and historical, economic and social contexts which
played a part in the evolving images of the 'Princess and the
pauper' (India); the 'Goodfellows' (Africa), and the 'Yellow peril'
(of China). Issues and questions are raised about the role of
literature for the young in the dissemination of the ideas and values

of the majority culture, and in particular, the role that such literature has played in propagating and sustaining beliefs and myths about race and nationality both then and in present day society.

Coleman, Joyce *Public Reading And The Reading Public In Late Medieval England And France* 250p. Cambridge: Cambridge University Press. ISBN Hb. 0-521553911 £37.50. In US, $59.95.
Although this book is published as part of the *Cambridge Studies in Medieval Literature*, its place in this guide is assured by the analysis of the nature of the reading public, and the nature of reading. The evidence leads Joyce Coleman to a major critique of the work of Walter Ong (and a large group associated with his overall position) concerning the division between oral and written language and the consequences for both intellectual development and societal development. Coleman comprehensively reviews the debate and then provides (through historical ethnography) rich and illuminating data relating to reports of reading behaviour from both England and France, to Chaucer's depictions of reading and his references to audience reception of his work, and to other secular literature of the period. This book is an important addition to the recent anthropological, social and psychological revaluations of the relationship between literacy and oracy.

Cook, Elizabeth *Epistolary Bodies: Gender And Genre In The Eighteenth-Century Republic Of Letters* 287p. Stanford, California: Stanford University Press. ISBN Hb. 0804725381 $32.50. In the UK and outside North America this book is distributed by Cambridge University Press. Hb. £27.95.
This book studies the eighteenth-century genre of the epistolary novel, in other words texts based around the letter as device for conveying narrative. Thus the book is first and foremost a study of literary texts rather than literacy per se. Nevertheless, the written letter as a fairly fundamental form of communication makes this book of interest from a literacy perspective. The epistolary narrative gains a major part of its power from the understanding of readers of the forms, and meanings of the act of letter writing, an

activity somewhat neglected by literacy researchers. The letters within a epistolary novel occupy a kind of halfway house between the registers and associations of personal letter production and the formal constructions of shaped literary texts. In her analyses of the novels, Cook (who writes extremely elegantly) is primarily concerned about their status as literature, but in the process she raises not only issues about literature but many issues about the nature of letter writing itself.

Corns, Thomas and Loewenstein, David *The Emergence Of Quaker Writing: Dissenting Literature In Seventeenth-Century England* 148p. London: Frank Cass. ISBN Pb. 0714642460 £16.00. In the US, $22.50. (1995)
This modest-sized, but very interesting collection of papers offers a rich overview of the ways in which writing (and not just books) had a seminal role in the development of the Quaker movement in England. Quaker writing, in the form of letters, polemical tracts, spiritual autobiographies, journals, essays, testimonies, and accounts of sufferings, helped, according to the editors, 'consolidate, shape, and authorise the movement and its culture'. Given the emancipatory achievement of early Quakerism the chapters which focus on women's writing are of particular interest. This volume shows clearly how literacy is intrinsically ideological, being rooted at every level in the belief systems of the Quaker movement.

Davis, Courtney *Celtic Ornament: Art And The Scribe* 96p. London: Blanford. ISBN Hb. 0713726105 £14.99. In the US, $24.95.
Courtney Davies provides a modern interpretation of the art of Celtic scribes in his black and white illustrations drawn from a range of famous manuscripts and other ornamentation. The text is divided into a series of short simple sections, each of which provides a brief introduction to such topics as the Celtic monasteries, the scriptorium, pens, pigments and the illuminated letter. There are also sections on various famous texts such as the Lindisfarne Gospel and the Book of Kells. Each section is only a few hundred words long and so is suited to absolute beginners, including children.

Demeude, Hugues *The Animated Alphabet* 176p. London: Thames and Hudson. ISBN **Pb.** 050027908X £14.95. In the USA, $24.95.

Thames and Hudson have produced a number of very richly illustrated books associated with the topic of literacy (see last year's volume of the guide) and they have now produced another. This is a book about the art of writing where the emphasis is on *art*. The author shares his passion for decorated letters, and he has collected these from a wide range of sources. Religious manuscripts of the eighth century are alongside picture postcards of the early 20 century. The book is mainly illustrations, which are beautifully presented, but these are collected into sections and accompanied by short but informative text. The sections include, the decorated initial or illuminated letters, letters created with human bodies, framed letters and a selection of illustrated alphabets. Those already familiar with this topic will find many old favourites reproduced in this truly sumptuous 'coffee table' volume.

Fairclough, Norman *Critical Discourse Analysis: The Critical Study Of Language* 265p. London: Longman. ISBN Hb. 0582219809 £40.00. ISBN Pb. 0582219841 £15.99. In the USA, Pb. $20.80. **(1995)**

This book is a collection of papers written by Norman Fairclough between 1983 and 1992. It is extremely helpful to have this important set of papers drawn together in one volume. While like Bernstein's work (see Atkinson above), Fairclough's field is primarily to do with the nature of language and power in general rather than literacy, his work has encompassed written texts (particularly the notion of critical literacy) and most of what he has to say about language in general has specific relevance for all language use whether written or oral. The book is divided into four sections: language, ideology and power; discourse and sociocultural change; textual analysis in social research; and critical language awareness.

Gamble, Harry *Books And Readers In The Early Church: A History Of Early Christian Texts* 337p. New Haven: Yale University Press. ISBN Hb. 0300060246 £19.95. In the US, Hb. $32.50. **(1995)**
The importance of the book in the development of the major religions has often been noted, but in this detailed and thorough study, the author examines a whole set of wider questions about the book in early Christianity. These questions address the the nature of the physical form of early Christian texts, how and by whom they were transcribed, how were they published and publicised, how they were duplicated and disseminated, how they were stored, collected and used, and who actually read them and in what circumstances. By doing so the author has gone beyond traditional concerns with the nature of the texts themselves to a more sociological examination of the wider issues of book production and use. While at first glance this book has a rather specialised and narrow focus, by asking these broader questions the author illuminates a whole range of important issues concerned with the relationships between literacy and the development of organised religion.

Gee, James *Social Linguistics And Literacies: Ideology In Discourses* (Rev. Ed.) 218p. London: Taylor and Francis. ISBN Hb. 0748404996 £39.00 ISBN Pb. 0748405003 £13.95. In the US, Pb. $25.95.
This is a second edition of a highly influential book first published in 1990. The book has been rewritten in its entirety rather than just having had a few changes, so it, in effect, constitutes a new book. The book offers an overview of sociocultural approaches to language and literacy, introduces a particular way of analysing language-in-use-in-society, and develops a specific theory of language and literacy situated within the notion of Discourses. The book develops this theory with specific reference to cross-cultural issues in communities and schools. This a major contribution to study in this field.

Gellrich, Jesse *Discourse And Dominion In The Fourteenth Century: Oral Contexts Of Writing In Philosophy, Politics, and Poetry* 304p. Princeton, New Jersey: Princeton University Press. ISBN Hb. 0691037493 $42.50. In the UK, £32.95. **(1995)**
One of the most dynamic areas of debate in recent years has been the historical relationship between orality and literacy. This book is centrally involved in this debate as it argues that while in fourteenth century England the use and influence of literacy was increasing dramatically, that rather than simply contributing to the demise of the oral tradition, orality itself was playing a significant role in the emergence of a literate tradition. Gellrich uses philosophical, historiographical and poetic written texts to demonstrate that oral communicative characteristics survived, although modified, in those texts. This literacy did not replace the oral tradition but, in some respects, imitated it. It is the unpacking of this notion in very fine detail that constitutes the principal task of this volume. This book might be usefully read in conjunction with that of Coleman (see above).

Giles, Judy and Middleton, Tim (Eds.) *Writing Englishness 1900-1950: An Introductory Sourcebook On National Identity* 285p. London: Routledge. ISBN Hb. 0415114411 £45.00. ISBN Pb. 041511442X £13.99. **(1995)**
Literacy is so much taken for granted as an everyday phenomenon that sometimes the ways in which it is used are not fully appreciated. This book is a collection of contemporary writings which show writers exploring, and sometimes quite explicitly attempting to create, a sense of national identity. The pieces used in this book come from a very wide range of sources, including: fiction, poetry, radio broadcasts, government committees, newspapers and political pamphlets. What the volume illustrates clearly is the powerful role of literacy in the formation of national identities.

Goodman, Sharon and Graddol, David *Redesigning English: New Texts, New Identities* 250p. London: Routledge. ISBN Hb. 0415131235 £45.00 ISBN Pb. 0415131243 £12.99.

This is another in the new series associated with the Open University course 'The English language: past, present and future'. This volume explores the many new forms of text and display of text that have developed in the twentieth century, and in particular examines the relationship between these new text forms and identity and social relations. The topics within the book range from, 'Text, time and technology in news English', 'Visual English', 'English in Cyberspace', 'Market forces speak English', and 'Global English, global culture?" As in the other books in this series an overview essay is accompanied by a number of readings. The book is clearly designed, and has copious examples. It is an excellent introduction to an interesting topic.

Graff, Harvey *The Labyrinths Of Literacy: Reflections On Literacy Past And Present* (revised edition) 349p. Pittsburgh, PA: University of Pittsburgh Press. ISBN Pb. 0822955628 $22.50. In the UK this book is distributed by Eurospan, £17.95. **(1995)**

This is the second edition of the book first published by Falmer Press in 1987, and containing six new chapters. These chapters, mostly published originally as individual papers, explore and make explicit 'the historicity, complexity, problematic nature and conditions of literacy whether our gaze turns to past or present or seeks to connect them'. It is, perhaps, this power of Graff's to connect the past with the present that makes this book so valuable in understanding current debates about literacy. The book is divided into four sections, the first being a single chapter reflection on the history of literacy, the second section explores past and present ideologies underpinning literacy debates and practices, and the third provides perspectives on the social situating of literacy. The final section's chapters provide for general reflections about the study of the history of literacy and lessons to be learnt from its study.

Harris, David *A Society Of Signs* 234p. London: Routledge. ISBN Hb. 0415111285 £42.00. Pb. 0415111283 £12.99. This book offers an an introduction to current debates around the themes of cultural identity and lifestyle. The book summarises and discusses some basic approaches in social theory and cultural analysis and offers specific readings of thinkers such as Barthes and Giddens. Aimed at students in cultural studies, media and sociology, the book gives access to a wide range of ideas. It is connected to literacy studies in that questions of culture, text and language are discussed.

Harris, Roy (Ed.) *The Origin Of Language* 332p. Bristol: Thoemmes Press. ISBN Hb. 1855064383 £45.00. ISBN Pb. 1855064375 £14.95. In the USA, Hb. $72.00. Pb. $24.95. This book offers a collection of speculative essays, written between 1851 and 1892, on the mystery of the origin of language, a mystery which remains unsolved today. The accounts in the collection construct an often impassioned debate which ran through the nineteenth century, and had at its centre the hottest social, spiritual and political issues of the time. The key question in this debate was posed by Darwin as to whether the fact of man's possession of language does or does not conflict with the notion that the human species evolved from some lower form. Although these essays are focused on oral language, they should be of interest to anyone interested in the history of oral and written language as the essential questions explored are applicable to both.

Hinds, Hilary *God's Englishwoman: Seventeenth-Century Radical Sectarian Writing And Feminist Criticism* 264p. Manchester: Manchester University Press. ISBN Hb. 0719048869 £35.00. ISBN Pb. 0719048877 £14.99. This book uses a number of perspectives from feminist literary criticism to examine the writing done by seventeenth century women who were members of radical sects (see also Corns and Loewenstein above). Using texts that have often been seen as non-literary (tracts, prophecies and spiritual autobiographies) Hinds shows how seventeenth century women writers were (a) very prolific and (b) more importantly, positioned themselves right at the heart of many religious, political, social and linguistic debates.

Participation in such issues was controversial and often dangerous, but despite this the impetus to represent their views in writing drive these women forward. Hinds very successfully seeks to alert readers to the existence and importance of these female writers in an historical period which those who study women's writing have undervalued and neglected. Hind's concern is principally with these texts as legitimate literary genres, but they are clearly also of considerable interest as demonstrations of powerful ideological literacy practices.

Hobbs, Catherine *Nineteenth-Century Women Learn To Write* 343p. Charlottesville: University Press of Virginia. ISBN Hb. 0813916054 $47.50. Distributed in the UK by Eurospan, £42.95. **(1995)**
While the role of women in the history of literacy has often been acknowledged, how women used literacy and how they went about achieving it has been less studied. This valuable book focuses on how nineteenth-century American women, in a time which stressed domesticity, piety and submissiveness, used literacy to achieve strength and power, a position which, according to the editor, was not achieved again until the 1960s. In Part One the chapters focus on the the cultures and contexts in which women learned to write, including ideological, institutional and informal contexts (and this includes a look at the 'semi-colon club'). In Part Two the chapters focus on the texts produced by women, and considers their distinctive voices, including African American women, female diarists, military wives, and those women who went into higher education.

Hooker, J. T. (Ed.) *Reading The Past: Ancient Writing From Cuneiform To The Alphabet* 384p. London: British Museum Press. ISBN Pb. 0714180777 £10.99 (1st paperback edition, 1996)
This book was first published in 1990 but this is the first paperback edition. There could not be a finer testimony to the problems of language historians than their efforts for centuries to try and describe and explain the development of written language. Controversies abound but the uncovering of what were for the most past indecipherable scripts has led to fresh insights and reappraisals. This book collects together six shorter booklets

published independently by the British Museum Press which provide an up-to-date exposition of a range of written scripts, their decipherment and their relationship to other scripts. The chapters cover: cuneiform; Egyptian Hieroglyphs; Linear B; The early alphabet; Greek inscriptions; and Etruscan writing.

Hymes, Dell *Ethnography, Linguistics, Narrative Inequality: Towards An Understanding Of Voice* 258p. London: Taylor and Francis. ISBN Hb. 074803477 £39.00 ISBN Pb. 0748403485 £14.95. In the USA, Hb. $75.00. Pb. $23.95. This book, in the publishers' series 'Critical Perspectives on Literacy and Education' is a collection of Dell Hymes's work published since 1972. A considerable amount of new material has been added, and revisions have been made to give a sense of unity to the collection. Hymes has had a scattered impact across the social sciences, most effectively on social anthropology, but is perhaps ultimately centrally concerned with education research on language behaviours. The book is divided into three sections reflecting Hymes's concerns with, as he explains: "ethnography as an approach, linguistics as a field, and narrative as a human accomplishment." Through wide-ranging critiques and presentations of his own and many others' work ranging across these topics, he discusses how theory and research in education and certain associated disciplines can be used to understand how particular discourses, languages and literacies count and act in particular cultures' and community's interests.

Kapitzke, Cushla *Literacy And Religion: The Textual Politics And Practice Of Seventh-Day Adventism* 343p. Amsterdam: John Benjamins Publishing Company. ISBN Hb. 9027217939 Hfl. 135.00. In the USA, ISBN 1556193181 $79.00. In the UK, Hb.£50.00. **(1995)**
In recent years increased interest in literacy as a socially embedded phenomenon has led to a number of studies which have examined in great detail the literacy practices of particular communities. This study continues this new tradition by exploring in depth one Seventh-day Adventist community in Northern Australia. The first part of the book explores in detail the interrelationships between diversities in literacies and religious belief. The second part is the

ethnographic investigation of the 'Riverside' community, of which the author is a member. Those who have read with interest Shirley Brice Heath's account of the 'Roadville' community, or Fishman's study of Amish literacy will find Kapitzke's rich, insightful and detailed study fascinating and rewarding. Her books shows just how socially complex is the literacy behaviour of people within the 'Riverside' community, and it is deeply and intrinsically wedded within the beliefs and concerns of that community. It is yet another powerful challenge to the notion that literacy exists as a discrete and independent phenomenon.

Keller-Cohen, Deborah (Ed.) Literacy: *Interdisciplinary Conversations* 429p. New Jersey: Hampton Press. ISBN Hb. 1881303489 $69.50; ISBN Pb. 1881303497 $27.50. Distributed in the UK by Eurospan (1994)
This book is part of a series called 'Written Language', edited by Marcia Farr which examines the characteristics of writing in the human world, across time and space. Here, scholars from 14 different fields offer insights into the social embeddedness of literacy. The book grew out of a conference called, 'Literacy Identity and Mind' held at the University of Michigan in 1991. The book includes a wide variety of topics, many of which combine discourse analysis with ethnography, for example Courtney Cazden discusses contrasting ideologies of writing instruction while Daniel Wagner looks at literacy acquisition. Many essays offer insights into literacy in different historical periods including the 17th and 18th centuries in America, Anglo Saxon England and 19th century women's clubs, and from different geographical areas including Turkey and Latin America. The result is a rich collection of essays, often in conversation with each other, as the title suggests, with many points of interest for the literacy scholar.

King, Russell., Connell, John and White, Paul (Eds.) *Writing Across Worlds: Literature And Migration* 284p. London: Routledge. ISBN Hb. 0415105293 £45.00. ISBN Pb. 0415105307 £14.99. In the USA, Hb. $69.95. Pb. $18.95. (1995)
This book stands at an interesting intersection of the social, the geographical and the literary. It is a collection of essays which use a

range of sources to discuss notions of migration. It is perhaps at the edge of the interest of this guide, but nevertheless reveals the significance of many socially embedded texts in documenting the changing patterns of human life. This is particularly evident in the way the editors, in their preface, document what they term the 'evolutionary series of forms of migrant literature', and this runs from ethnic newsletters, diaries, letter songs and oral narratives, right through to highly literary forms in which migrants now influence the cultures of their adopted countries. It is a very interesting and illuminating book.

Kintgen, Eugene *Reading In Tudor England* 242p. Pittsburgh: University of Princeton Press. ISBN Hb. 0822939398 $40.00. Distributed in the UK by Eurospan, £31.95.
Just as language itself has changed across several centuries so the way people understand and use written language has shifted. In this book, Kintgen uses a number of Tudor texts to explore what reading meant to people in that period, and does so by considering the education of children in grammar schools who were taught to read primarily through Latin texts, the influence of reading in religious settings on those who did not receive a grammar school education, a look at three educated readers, and an examination of the advice offered by self-help books (in English). The author spends time in the introduction setting out a view of reading as a highly individualised activity, and a psychological process, and yet at the same time provides massive evidence throughout the book of the socially embedded nature of the activity.

Kress, Gunther and Van Leeuwen, Theo *Reading Images: The Grammar Of Visual Design* 288p. London: Routledge. ISBN Hb. 0415105994 £49.99. ISBN Pb. 0415106001 £14.99. In the USA, Hb. $74.95. Pb. $22.95.
This book addresses the crucial question of communication in a time when increasingly the visual has come to predominate. The authors contest that increasingly visual media are to be 'read' like writing, and that we need a 'grammar' in order to deal with the new semiotic landscape. Using examples from children's drawings, science text books, advertisements and newspapers, the authors argue convincingly that times have changed, and we need to re-

frame our understanding of literacy and literacies. An essential book for those wanting to keep up with the new debates around literacy in the twenty-first century.

Lechte, John *Writing And Psychoanalysis: A Reader* 213p. London: Arnold. ISBN Hb. 034064561X £40.00. ISBN: Pb. 0340624891 £14.99. In the USA, Hb. $49.95. Pb. $18.95.
This book, although on the margins of the scope of this guide, will be of interest to those interested in the contribution modern post-structuralist thought concerned with psychoanalysis can make to our understanding of aspects of the writing process. In the view of the editor, developed through contributions from Freud and others' work from the last forty years, psychoanalysis has developed from a relatively positivist theory and practice into a poetic discourse. In parallel perhaps, its foremost practitioners have conceived of the writing of fiction as displacement and then, more recently, as a way of exploring the divisions inherent in subjectivity. The writing of fiction, then, is considered as a form of identification, through which is explored the permeability of the subject-object divide. Translations of works by Foucault and Kristeva on madness, literature and psychoanalysis appear here for the first time in English.

Livingston, Eric *An Anthropology Of Reading* 161p. Bloomington: Indiana University Press. ISBN Hb. 0253335094 $27.95. Distributed in the UK by Open University Press £21.95. **(1995)**
This book represents the effort of the author to open up the practice of reading for critical scrutiny and reveal the phenomenon of reading itself. It starts from the position that reading is work and is thus susceptible to anthropological investigation. It is a very complex and detailed book which concentrates on literary reading, arguing that the practices of the ordinary reader and that of the literary reader are different in many respects. Literary reading is perceived to be a special alchemy of laic reading practices, "which both sustain the critical enterprise and irreparably distort ordinary reading".

Lodge, David *The Practice Of Writing* 340p. London: Secker and Warburg. ISBN Hb. 043620488 £20.00. Pb. 0436204088 £12.99. In the USA published by Viking Penguin. Pb. $24.95.
This volume encompasses a variety of genres with a unity of theme; the meeting of 'fact' and fiction in the process of creative writing. The texts considered are drawn from novels and drama (plus a TV adaptation) written in English during the twentieth century. Although Lodge writes lucidly, if in this collection either briefly or semi-satirically, on modernist and postmodern influences on the novel, he inclines particularly towards an evolved version of the naturalistic tradition. This preference is characteristic of his own novels. In writing about these and others' works Lodge is chiefly concerned with the experiences, especially (auto)biographical, and opinions which are transmuted into the stuff of fiction.

Lucas, John *Writing And Radicalism* 351p. New York: Addison Wesley Longman. ISBN Hb. 0582214149 $Price unknown ISBN Pb. 0582214157 $Price unknown.
This book is part of a general series called 'crosscurrents' which adopts an interdisciplinary approach in response to increasing modularisation in school and college courses. The book includes a very wide variety of material, including articles on Milton, women printers in the 17th century, writers at the time of the French Revolution, Chartism and during key historical events such as the General Strike and the Spanish Civil War. Each piece is very different, and there is no unifying style. Literacy is not the focus so much as literary texts; however, the writing and printing described in the book is a testimony to the power of literacy. The book has an unequivocally radical approach, and to historians of literacy will make lively reading.

MacDonald, Myra *Representing Women: Myths Of Femininity In The Popular Media* 250p. London: Arnold. ISBN Pb. 0340632216 £12.99. (1995)
This book draws on texts within popular media to discuss myths of femininity and critically explores gender in relation to the media. Taking theories from Freud and Lacan the book discusses a variety of texts including those from television, advertising and film. The author also takes issue with contemporary cultural discourses such

as those found in women's magazines. A stimulating read for those interested in cultural studies and feminism.

Maybin, Janet and Mercer, Neill *Using English: From Conversation To Cannon* 326p. London: Routledge. ISBN Hb. 0415131197 £45.00. ISBN Pb. 0415131200 £12.99. In the US, Hb. $65.00. Pb. $24.95.
This is one of a series of four substantial volumes prepared by members of the course team for the Open University course, 'The English language: past present and future'. This book is dedicated to studying the diversity of uses of the English language, in different modes, channels, literatures, social contexts, cultural settings and parts of the world, by both native and non-native speakers. Each chapter begins with a specially commissioned study of its theme, this being supplemented by selection of readings representing different standpoints and authorative studies. The book is well-illustrated with a full-colour section and assumes no previous knowledge of linguistics. It is a well-designed and accessible book.

Mitton, Roger *English Spelling And The Computer* 207p. London: Longman. ISBN Hb. 0582234794 £35.00. ISBN Pb. 0582234786 £12.99. In the USA, Pb. $27.40.
This book is based upon the author's Ph.D. which was principally designed to produce a better computer spell check. The first half of the book surveys spelling itself, offering a history of the spelling system, exploring the debate between those who advocate spelling reform and those who don't, and examining many different types of spelling error. The second half of the book focuses upon attempts to develop a spell checker for word processing packages which would have greater potential than those currently available, and describes a system which which has been developed by the author of this book.

Myers, Robin and Harris, Michael *A Genius For Letters: Books And Bookselling From The 16th To The 20th Century* Winchester: St. Pauls Bibliographies. ISBN Hb. 1873040245 £25.00. In the USA, Delaware: Oak Knoll Press. ISBN 1-884718167 $30.00. (1995)
The history of literacy cannot be told without the stories of

booksellers, and the papers in this book (which resulted from a small conference on the topic) make a welcome contribution to knowledge about this relatively understudied area. Nine contributors cover a variety of topics ranging from the relationship between booksellers and bookbinders, a fascinating account of bookselling in seventeenth-century London, studies of particular booksellers, and selling books through libraries, booksellers and book clubs. Despite the specialised nature of some of these topics, they turned out to be extremely interesting and mostly very accessible to the interested but non-specialist reader.

Prinsloo, Mastin and Breier, Mignonne (Eds.) *The Social Uses Of Literacy: Theory And Practice In Contemporary South Africa* 279p. Bertram, South Africa: Sached Books, and Amsterdam: John Benjamins. ISBN Europe Hb. 9027217955 £48.00 Pb. 9027217963 £20.00. In the USA, Hb. 1556193203 $69.00 Pb. 1556193211 $24.50.
This book explores the social uses of literacy in a variety of settings in South Africa. It provides a challenge to an assumption in educational policy that those without schooling represent a homogeneous and disabled group. The chapters are situated in post-apartheid South Africa's attempts to develop mass provision for adult literacy education. Such demand was policy led rather than consumer led, and as the chapters in this book reveal, the failure to understand the embedded nature of literacy use by various communities, limited their influence and effect. The chapters are grouped in three sections: Literacies at work; Mediating literacies; and Contextualising literacies. Together they represent a major addition to the work on understanding the meanings literacy has for people in their lives.

Reddick, Allen *The Making Of Johnson's Dictionary (Rev. Ed.)* 251p. Cambridge: Cambridge University Press. ISBN Pb. 0521568382 £13.95. In the USA, $17.95.
This a revised second edition of Reddick's book (first published in 1990) and is the first paperback edition. Johnson's dictionary has a special place in the history of written language (as well as an almost mythical place in English history and identity), and Reddick's finely detailed analysis reveals just how cognitively and procedurally complex was its development, production and

revision. The book not only offers a detailed narrative account of conception, composition and revision, but in the process shows how Johnson wrestled (sometimes successfully and sometimes not) with conceptual problems relating to the nature of an enterprise which tries to codify language, and fix it within the covers of a book; a problem which Johnson in his preface declared to be impossible. As Reddick puts it, "Johnson's dictionary provides an ever-fascinating image and product of struggle, desire, difficulty and possibility." However it is Reddick's diligence and clarity which enables the reader to understand just how much this is so. (see also Green - Reference books about literacy section)

Reynolds, Susanne *Medieval Reading: Grammar, Rhetoric And The Classical Text* 235p. Cambridge: Cambridge University Press. ISBN Hb. 0521472571 £35.00. In the USA, $54.95. **(1996)**
This very detailed and complex book explores the glosses (in effect commentaries) on the classic texts that formed an essential part of becoming literate in the middle ages. Reynolds's central concern is to ask not what these glosses reveal about the classic texts but what kind of reading and reader is implied within these glosses; in other words, what kind of reading process was being constructed by the authors of the glosses. The book shows how the reading of classical texts was shaped by the demands of acquiring Latin literacy. A background in Latin is probably a help with the book although the substance of the arguments can be understood without it.

Simon, Sherry *Gender In Translation: Cultural Identity And The Politics Of Transmission* 195p. London: Routledge. ISBN Hb. 0415115351 £35.00. ISBN Pb. 0415115361 £12.99. In the USA, Hb. $59.95. Pb. $18.95.
This book, by a Canadian writer, explores translation not simply as a technical skill (about which there would be no disagreement) but as explicit literary activism. Thus it explore the ways in which translators contribute to cultural debates and open up new lines of transmission. The precise focus of the book is the issue of gender in this activism. This does not mean the gender of the translator so much as the ways in which gender as a cultural phenomenon is transmitted through translation. The book begins with an overview of gendered positions in translation, explores feminist translation,

particularly how French feminism was exported to North America, and explores the relationship between culture and translation.

Srikant, Sarangi and Slembrouck, Stefan *Language, Bureaucracy And Social Control* 242p. London: Longman. ISBN Hb. 058208623X £38.00. ISBN Pb. 0582086221 £14.99. Although the central focus of this book is about the interrelationship of language, bureaucracy and social control rather than directly about literacy, clearly literate language is a prime feature in such relationships. The authors offer a detailed examination of distinctive and powerful language practices of modern institutions, both state and private. The theoretical components are fully supported by detailed case study material taken from a number of countries which enable the authors to examine their topic from a number of different positions particularly individual as well as institutional. This is an important addition to a growing body of work on critical discourse analysis.

Taylor, Insup and Martin Taylor, M. *Writing And Literacy In Chinese, Korean And Japanese* 412p. Amsterdam: John Benjamins Publishing Company. ISBN Hb. 9027217947 Hfl.120.00. In the USA, ISBN 155619319X Hb. $68.00. In the UK, £48.00. **(1995)**
There are many books on the history and nature of writing systems but most tend to concentrate on the development of Western scripts. Yet the countries of the far East have distinctive, and ancient writing systems and more deserves to be known about them. This book covers three such systems and for each offers an account of the history, how it relates to spoken language, how it is learned and taught, how it is used in daily life, how it can be computerised, and how it relates to the literacy, education and culture of its users, past and present. It is thus more than a book about writing systems as it positions them firmly in their cultural context. All three systems are related and all have been faced with tensions as the communicative demands of the modern world have led to attempts to create systems that are easier to learn. The book has been written less for the scholar and more for the interested lay person, and in that respect it is extremely successful, providing an interesting and informative account of writing in these countries.

Tinkler, Penny *Constructing Girlhood: Popular Magazines For Girls Growing Up In England 1920-1950* 209p. London: Taylor and Francis. ISBN Hb. 0748402853 £38.00. ISBN Pb. 0748402861 £12.95. In the US, Hb. $75.00. Pb. $24.95. **(1995)**
The contribution to the formation of identity by the popular media is a subject of increasing study (see also Beetham, this volume). In this book Tinkler explores the influence of girls' magazines during the first half of this century. It is essentially a study of gender and the ways in which these magazines contributed to the social construction of female adolescence. Tinkler pays particular attention to age and class and considers these in both historical and biographical contexts. Adolescence is a period of considerable change - the transition from school to work, and the move into heterosexual relationships and onward to marriage and motherhood - and the book documents in considerable detail, and very interestingly, how the changing form and content of the magazines was determined by the 'articulation of the interests of capital and of patriarchy'.

Tonfoni, Graziella with Richardson, James *Writing As A Visual Art* 189p. Oxford: Intellect. ISBN Hb. 1871516382 £19.95. In the USA, published by Croomland, $29.95. **(1994)**
This book is aimed at anyone engaged in the writing process who is interested in exploring certain aspects of the visual creation of text. Tonfoni's preoccupation is using shapes: as useful metaphors in the structuring of texts; in the generation of ideas and other parts of the creative process; and in the production of the finished text, for instance writing on a cube or pyramid. Calligraphy, printing and many other elements of design are not covered. The book, which was written by J. Richardson after conversations with the Italian academic, G. Tonfoni, is highly prescriptive, mostly concerning what writers should think about, in a visual dimension, as they write. It has fifty black and white illustrations, chiefly intended as stimuli for writing activities.

Unger, J. Marshall *Literacy And Script Reform In Occupation Japan: Reading Between The Lines* 176p. New York: Oxford University Press. ISBN Hb. 0195101669 $39.95. In the UK, Hb. £27.50.

At first sight this book looks like one for a minority audience. In fact, it is a fascinating account of the politics and history of literacy within a particularly distinctive cultural setting. Despite dealing with a non-western script, the author has made this work perfectly accessible to the interested but non-specialist reader. The book discusses efforts after the second world war to introduce a Japanese alphabetic writing system, particularly to help Japanese children make faster progress in non-language subjects such as mathematics. Unger explains how the project was killed off by a combination of US military influence and the Japanese Ministry of Education. The story of the efforts to erase the project could stand comfortably alongside the story told by Brian Cox (see last year's edition of the guide) about efforts by the British Government to manipulate evidence in pursuit of policy change.

Zunder, William and Trill, Suzanne (Eds.) *Writing And The English Renaissance* 351p. London: Longman. ISBN Hb. 058222974X £38.00. ISBN Pb. 0582229758 £16.99. In the USA Hb. $58.50. Pb. $25.95.

This book is one of series, 'crosscurrents' which aims to explore an area through offering essays discussing contemporary texts. It is somewhat on the fringe of the concerns of this guide, but nevertheless it is through the writing of the Renaissance that the reader is able to explore the nature and richness of Renaissance culture. While the book is rooted in English studies, the essays and the texts discussed draw from a wide range of critical enquiries.

Reference books about literacy

Coulmas, Florian *The Blackwell Encyclopedia Of Writing Systems* 603p. Oxford: Blackwells. ISBN Hb. 0631194460 £65.00. In the USA, $75.95.

This an extraordinarily comprehensive book about writing systems. The title indicates the specific focus; it is not about writing as a social, educational, or psychological act. It is guided by an overriding premise that writing systems are linguistic systems. In addition to extensive coverage of the world's writing systems (current and past), the entries also include a range of phenomena associated with writing systems which turn the Encyclopedia into an even more useful book. The Encyclopedia is copiously illustrated with pictures and tables. Entries are cross referenced and many sections include a couple of suggestions for further reading. While it is not really a book for sustained reading, it is difficult not to continue once one has started to dip into it. The entries are very clearly written yet are concise. We owe Florian Coulmas and Blackwell thanks for producing this wonderful book which should be on the shelves of all academic libraries alongside his previous book *The Writing Systems Of The World*.

Enos, Theresa *Encyclopedia Of Rhetoric And Composition: Communication From Ancient Times To The Information Age* 803p. New York: Garland Publishing Inc. ISBN Hb. 0824072006 $95.00.
This extraordinary and immense volume sets out to provide an introduction to 'rhetoric, including the major periods and personages, concepts and applications' across a two-and-a-half-thousand-year period. It has 167 entries ranging from single paragraphs (as on 'periphrasis') to many substantial essays (as on 'persuasion'). A work such as this, with its comprehensiveness and detail will be of interest to people in many fields. It is pretty well impossible to turn to any topic and not find a well-written, informative and interesting entry. Most entries offer a bibliography for further enquiry, and there is substantial cross-referencing. While it essentially a work of reference, great enjoyment can be had by just dipping into the pages and reading whatever appears. It is work of scholarship and its quality should ensure it remains a valuable tool for a long time to come.

Green, Jonathon *Chasing The Sun: Dictionary-Makers And The Dictionaries They Made* 423p. London: Jonathon Cape ISBN Hb. 0224040103 £25.00. ISBN Pb. 0712662162 £15.00. In the US, published by Holt and Co., Pb. $30.00
This very substantial book traces the development of dictionaries, and tells the stories of the people who created them. The level of detail makes the book something to dip into rather than read all the

way through, but as an overall history it is invaluable. The author manages to cover about four-and-a-half thousand years in his four hundred pages, ranging from early bilingual word lists right up to a Random House College dictionary of 1991. Along the way, he alerts the reader to range of fundamental issues relating to lexicography: what exactly counts as dictionary, the role of plagiarism, and ideological concerns (in particular with obscenity and taboos). The author's special interest in slang leads him to devote a fair amount of space to dictionaries on this topic, perhaps rather too much in the space available. This is a very useful history of a genre which has always provoked argument but we would be hard-pressed to do without. (see also Reddick - section 1)

Wientraub, Samuel (Ed.) *Annual Summary Of Investigations Relating To Reading: July 1994 - June 1995* 193p. Newark, Delaware: International Reading Association. ISBN Pb. 0872072401 $28.95.
This the latest in the long series of summaries published by the International Reading Association. Once again it provides carefully written, detailed summaries of most published research in the field of reading and related areas. The scope is quite wide, ranging from easily identified conventional areas, psychology, teaching etc, to topics such as newspapers, censorship and physiology. This annual publication is without doubt a seminal source book for anyone interested in literacy.

Educational books about literacy

General

Allen, Karen and Miller, Margery *Purposeful Reading And Writing: Strategies In Context* 162p. Orlando, Florida: Harcourt Brace College Publishers. ISBN Pb. 0155011642 $34.70. (1995)
This book, aimed at teachers of children from grade 4-8, explores approaches to literacy teaching which promote an integrative and thematic curriculum. The aim is to offer children the same sense of purposefulness that operates in the reading and writing lives of

adults. It centres on purpose, audience and organisation, and thus is, although not mentioning the term, a kind of introduction to rhetoric. The authors encourage children to explore these areas through examining actual examples of text forms, examining their construction and organisation and then developing their own examples.

Anders, Patricia and Guzzetti, Barbara *Literacy Instruction In The Content Areas* 189p. Orlando, Florida: Harcourt Brace College Publishers. ISBN Pb. 015500820X No Price available.
Written for undergraduate, graduate and in-service teachers who work with children from kindergarten through to grade 12, this book is for educators who wish to integrate the literacy process with content (subject) area teaching. The authors believe that educators who understand literacy and can organise teaching to enable children to use literacy to learn are best able to organise subject teaching in a way that children will be able to understand. They do not believe that children need one set of reading strategies in science and another set in literature, history, mathematics or geography etc. The book gives examples of practices appropriate for several different subject areas. This book will be particularly useful for teachers who are using methods that are consistent with social constructivist, process or whole-language theories.

Antonacci, Patricia and Hedley, Carolyn (Eds.) *Natural Approaches To Reading And Writing* 202p. Norwood, New Jersey: Ablex Publishing Corporation. ISBN Hb. 0893917508 $42.50 ISBN Pb. 0893919225 $22.50. In the UK ISBN Hb. 0893917508 £32.50. ISBN Pb. 0893919225 £17.95.
This interesting collection of papers arose from a workshop at a New York State Reading Association conference. In Part One, the theme is the development of literacy, with chapters on theories of natural language, oral language, play and literacy, and portfolios for documenting young children's literacy. Part Two is concerned with specific approaches for developing literacy. Preliminary chapters explore the development of writing, and teaching writing in the primary grades. Teacher researchers contribute chapters on ways to empower readers in kindergarten, finding books for the interests and needs of young children, the role of metacognition, and literacy across the curriculum. Part Three looks at supporting the literacy

development of children by creating conducive environments, and empowering those concerned. Finally, there is a brief appendix of family literacy resources for the North American teacher.

Bernstein, Basil *Pedagogy, Symbolic Control And Identity: Theory, Research, Critique* 216p. London: Taylor and Francis. ISBN Hb. 074840371X £39.00. ISBN Pb. 0748403728 £14.95.

In this book, part of Falmer's 'Critical perspectives on language and education' series, Bernstein reviews his work on language and education, effectively summarising it for readers new to his theories. The first part of the book brings readers up-to-date with Bernstein's work, in particular the need to examine more closely the actual process of transmission. The second part contains a discussion about the principles of the methodology of his research into transmission as well as the languages of description, while the third part takes on his critics (and in which one of them gets to write a pretty lame reply). The direct and indirect influence of Bernstein on recent educational change in the Uk and elsewhere ought to make this very useful reading for those interested in pedagogy. It is an important book for those engaged in language and literacy education.

Bissex, Glenda *Partial Truths: A Memoir And Essays On Reading, Writing, And Researching* 220p. Portsmouth, New Hampshire: Heinemann. ISBN Pb. 0435072242 $25.00.

Those people interested in early literacy at the beginning of the 1980s will remember the revelation of Bissex's book 'Gnys at wrk'. In the current book Bissex provides a memoir and reproduces a number of her earlier essays. The memoir is the story of her life, focusing particularly on her involvement with literacy, and of considerable interest is the part where she provides background to the writing of the earlier book. It is interesting to note that her son Paul, the subject of that first book, was twenty-six when this one was being written and was able to act as a critical friend in its creation. The twelve essays, some very short, divide into two categories: those about writing and reading and those about the teacher as researcher.

Browne, Ann *Developing Language And Literacy 3-8*
288p. London: Paul Chapman Publishing. ISBN Pb.
1853962821 £13.95. In the, USA, Taylor and Francis $24.95.
In this book Browne seeks to bring early years language and literacy
education up-to-date in the light of recent educational changes in
the UK. It is a very detailed book with a wide range of informative
examples accompanied by some sensitive and sensible analysis and
interpretation. The scope of the book is comprehensive, covering
speaking and listening, transcriptional skills, bilingual learners,
gender, problems with language, parental involvement, and
assessment. The final chapters turn towards the development of
schemes of work and policies for language and literacy in the early
years. This is a well-written text suited to both intending teachers
and teachers who wish to deepen their knowledge of young
children's language and literacy.

Brumfit, Christopher *Language Education In The
National Curriculum* 239p. Oxford: Blackwells. ISBN Hb.
0631188991 £40.00. ISBN Pb. 0631189017 £12.99. In the
USA, Hb. $55.95. Pb. $22.95.
This book offers teachers a comprehensive, principled and critical
overview of all aspects of policy and practice related to language
work in the context of British educational change generally and the
National Curriculum in particular. Distinctively, the book aims to
provide a coherent critical account of recent educational policy and
the impact of associated legislation in all major areas of language
education, including: English as both mother tongue and second
language; foreign language; bilingual children and community
languages; drama; literature; literacy; media studies; and knowledge
about language. The book should help ensure that the decisions
taken by individual schools and teachers are shaped by an
accessible and coherent source of linguistically informed thinking
about language education.

Buckingham, David and Sefton-Green, Julian (Eds.) *Cultural Studies Goes To School: Reading And Teaching Popular Media* 229p. London: Taylor and Francis. ISBN Hb: 0748401997 ISBN Pb. 0748402004 £14.95. In the USA, Hb. $85.00. Pb. $29.00.

This is part of the 'Critical Perspectives on Literacy and Education' series edited by Allan Luke in Australia, and has a media studies theme while addressing itself to the concept of 'critical literacy'. The book is rooted in work developed with teenagers in an inner city classrooms around different aspects of contemporary culture. The authors argue that contemporary culture is largely electronically mediated, and that therefore literacy applies across a range of media. Chapters examining teenagers' interactions and engagement with rap, magazines, radio, posters and film develop the argument for becoming critically literate in a range of media and give practising media studies teachers a lively and inspirational point of departure for their work.

Christie, James; Enz, Billy, Vukelich, Carol *Teaching Language And Literacy: Preschool Through The Elementary Grades* 497p New York: Longman US. ISBN Pb.0673985539 No price available. (1997)

This is a substantial, detailed and very thorough book. It is also a very practical. The authors take a constructivist approach to children's learning, arguing that children learn about oral and written language by engaging in integrated, meaningful and functional activities with other people. The book has four main sections, apart from the introduction. They cover language and literacy learning during the pre-school years, language arts instruction at preschool and kindergarten, language arts instruction in the elementary grades, while the final section examines portfolios and home-school collaboration. The book contains case studies, classroom teachers' own comments and ideas, and special feature boxes with in-depth information. The book is clearly written, exceptionally well structured and highly informative. Although a North American book it would be of considerable interest to teachers in the UK.

Church, Susan *The Future Of Whole Language: Reconstruction Or Self-Destruction* 136p. Portsmouth, New Hampshire: Heinemann Books. ISBN Pb. 0435088823 $17.00. 'The Future of Whole Language' is this author's call to action - her plea is for all educators to become more overtly political. She believes that a whole language philosophy offers a powerful perspective through which we can transform classroom pedagogy, staff development, and educational reform. Drawing from her experiences as a teacher, curriculum supervisor, and senior manager, Church offers a critical analysis of approaches to teacher change, educational reform, and educational leadership that disempower teachers and students and result in only the appearance of change. She urges educators in all settings to take a critical stance and suggests that whole language must assume a more critical edge if it is to reach its potential as a force for positive change. Examples of how a whole language agenda is also a political agenda are provided. (See also Edelsky and Routman in this guide.)

Clipson-Boyles, Suzi *Supporting Language And Literacy: A Handbook For Those Who Assist In Early Years Settings* 88p. London: David Fulton Publishers. ISBN Pb. 1853464384 ££12.99. In the USA, Taylor and Francis Pb. $22.95. This is a well-presented and helpful handbook, aimed, as its subheading indicates, at 'those who assist in early years settings', a group for whom such accessible material is often hard to locate. Since the book is principally concerned with work in British educational settings, it includes discussion of the National Curriculum Orders for English, although it places these within a wider context. Theory is well illustrated with practical experience, and readers are encouraged to reflect upon their own experience through the use of activities suggested throughout the book. Activity sheets and ideas for group work are included, together with further reading at the end of each chapter.

Davies, Chris *What Is English Teaching?* 159p. Buckingham: Open University Press. ISBN Pb. 0335194788 £12.95. In the USA, Taylor and Francis $24.95. In juxtaposing what English teaching in the secondary school is with what it might be, Davies not only provides an illuminating account of its recent history with a breathtaking range of oscillating legal ramifications, but also offers helpful alternatives to current orthodoxies. Whilst not underwriting a pedagogy of benign relativism, Davies leaves the reader in no doubt about what he sees to be at the heart of English teaching: the development in learners of an explicit understanding and vision of what language can do for their own varied and complex needs. The inclusion of papers by three other people adds extra dimensions to a topic which will require a paradigmatic shift if it is to keep up with developments elsewhere in the world.

Donoahue, Zoe; Van Tassell, Mary and Paterson, Leslie *Research In The Classroom: Talk, Texts, And Inquiry* 131p. Newark, Delaware: International Reading Association. ISBN 0872071461 $18.00.
Teachers of literacy, along with many others, engage in classroom research. This book is a collection of work sharing some American teachers' explorations into the oral and written discourse of the students in their classrooms. The range of research questions explored includes interest in journal writing, conversation, and storytelling, as well as the common theme of the role of oral and written discourse within inquiry communities. It is presented in a style which will make these ideas accessible to teachers.

Edelsky, Carole *With Literacy And Justice For All: Rethinking The Social In Language And Education* (2nd Edition) 242p. London: Taylor and Francis. ISBN Hb. 0748405828 £39.00. ISBN Pb. 0748405836 £13.95. In the USA, Hb. $64.95. Pb. $22.95.
This is a second edition of the book first published in 1991. The principal difference is a new final chapter. This book, while North American, will be read with understanding in the UK as it is, on one level, a response to international shifts in thinking which are seeking to narrow down the curriculum and institutionalise practices which derive from some awkward beliefs about the nature and purpose of literacy. On a more fundamental level, it is a very powerful, passionate and closely argued case for an education system which is just, offers an equal education to all and does so in ways which are holistic and respect cultural values. It might be of interest to read this book alongside that by Routman (see later this section).

Gadsden, Vivian and Wagner, Daniel (Eds.) *Literacy Among African American Youth: Issues In Learning, Teaching and Schooling* 316p. New Jersey: Hampton Press. ISBN Hb. 1881303276 $59.50. ISBN Pb. 1-881303284 $22.95. **(1995)**

This book is a collection of papers that were discussed at a conference of the same name, sponsored by the Literacy Research Centre and the Graduate School of Education at the University of Pennsylvania. This brought together specialists in literacy and related fields to examine access to literacy by African-American youth. Discussion revolved around appropriate learning models and issues to which future research should respond. The book is divided into different sub sections - a background section on historical and contemporary perspectives; Literacy in home and school contexts; Literacy, school policy and classroom practice; and Literacy curriculum strategies. The authors all share a perspective of hope that the literacy curricula can meet the needs of African Americans.

Gillard, Marni *Storyteller, Storyteacher: Discovering The Power Of Storytelling For Teaching And Living* 214p. Yorke, Maine: Stenhouse Publishers. ISBN Pb. 1571100148 $18.50. Distributed in the UK by Paul Chapman Publishing £14.50.

This is a storyteller's own story. The author has spent a long career as a teacher and storyteller, developing a considerable reputation in North America for her artistry. This book tells the story of the sources and development of her art. It is also an educator's story and it therefore includes reflections and guidance on many points of professional principle, technique and resource. Notable passages discuss: the significant differences between storytelling and story reading; the role of storytelling in the development of the child; how to choose the 'right' story to tell; reasons and strategies for the use of visualisation; how less compliant readers or writers can find a safe path to literacy through oral storying, and how oral stories help build a sense of community.

Hall, Nigel and Martello, Julie (Eds.) *Listening To Children Think: Exploring Talk In the Early Years* 137p. London: Hodder and Stoughton. ISBN Pb. 0-340-65831-2 £10.99.
This book looks at the important role of talk in the lives of young children and at how educators of young children can discover so much about the children by listening to what they have to say. Each of ten different chapters investigate how creating space to listen to children thinking aloud offers insights into the power of children's minds. Each contributor presents a case study which shows children using talk to learn and reflect upon the world around them. While some of the chapters are exclusively about oral language, many examine oral language components of literacy activities such as learning to punctuate, storytelling, understanding authorial voice etc. James Britton said, "Reading and writing float on a sea of talk" and this book helps demonstrate how fundamental for literacy is children's use of language.

Hall, Nigel and Robinson, Anne (Eds.) *Learning About Punctuation* 174p. Clevedon: Multilingual Matters. ISBN Hb. 1853593222 £29.00. ISBN Pb. 1853593214 £9.90. In the USA it is published by Heinemann Books Pb. $24.95.
This book, said to be the "first ever book to study how people, especially children, make sense of punctuation" is not, as the editors are keen to point out, a book on how to punctuate but is one that examines how children and adults develop their own understanding of concepts relating to the learning and teaching of punctuation. It is a book that makes one begin to think in depth and raise questions about how punctuation is taught to young children and about how one uses punctuation in one's personal writing. The book has nine very varied and different chapters written by experts in their field from both Britain and America. Each chapter looks at learning about punctuation in a different way and covers work done with learners of varying ages. While not a book about teaching punctuation the chapters are, nevertheless, full of insights which raise issues for the teaching process.

Harp, Bill and Brewer, Jo Ann *Reading And Writing: Teaching The Connections* (2nd Ed.) 600p. Orlando, Florida: Harcourt Brace College Publishers. ISBN Hb. 0155009583 $40.00.

This is the second edition of this book and it includes many significant changes in relation to the teaching of literacy, all of which share the goal of creating classrooms where children learn to love reading and writing. The authors feel, however, that teaching children how to read and write is not enough and state that educators must create environments that invite children to read and write for real, communicative purposes. The authors espouse a whole language approach to literacy and for this second edition the book has been updated in relation to the research completed since the first edition was published in 1991. They quote a New Zealand colleague who feels that there are two kinds of teachers in the world: green and growing, or ripe and rotting. Harp and Brewer are working hard to stay green and growing and this book reflects their philosophy.

Hasan, Ruqaiya and Williams, Geoff (Eds.) *Literacy In Society* 431p. London: Longman. ISBN Pb. 058221792X £18.99.

This book, of mostly Australian origin, offers a variety of chapters which focus on literacy as a phenomenon which is socially situated. Most of the contributions are rooted on systemic linguistics (and indeed, were originally papers given at the 19th International Systemic Functional Congress of 1992). The chapters, which are mostly related to educational areas, range across curriculum subjects and across age groups. The position of the chapter authors is to challenge conventional literacy pedagogy as unidimensional and overly congruent with the beliefs and practices of empowered groups in society. The authors offer insights into how varying social contexts have different kinds of relationships with conventional schooling which are seldom understood by schools or the schooling system, and explore how pedagogy might change to accommodate to the ideological nature of out-of-school literacy knowledge.

Hilton, Mary (Ed.) *Potent Fictions: Children's Literacy And The Challenge Of Popular Culture* 196p. London: Routledge ISBN Pb. 0415135303 £9.99. In the USA, Pb. $16.50.

The background to this book is the belief that the nature of literacy is constantly shifting and that fundamental influences on an individual's literacy derive from their social, economic and cultural contexts. Consequently, literacy as it develops in the home is often very different from that fostered in education, where values attached to particular genres or even entire media may be entirely divergent. The contributors to this book, all with experience of teaching children and lecturing and/or writing in education, explore contemporary literacy as developing within popular culture. They argue for an understanding of this to be developed by teachers and incorporated into classroom work. Through encouraging the development of critical attitudes and use of positive aspects of popular, home-based toys and media, the bridge between literacy at home and school can be crossed with positive results for both spheres. The book includes analyses of contemporary examples of English popular culture, many of which are North American imports.

Kucer, Stephen., Silva, Cecilia and Delgado-Larocco, Esther *Curricular Conversations: Themes In Multicultural And Monolingual Classrooms* 185p. Yorke, Maine: Stenhouse Publishers. ISBN Pb. 157100164 $19.50. Distributed in the UK by Paul Chapman Publishing £15.95. (1995)

This USA publication is written for teachers. It takes the idea of teaching through 'themes' and explores the potential for developing literacy in a range of genres through theme work. It argues for this whole view of literacy rather than teaching isolated 'constituents'. This book draws on, and aims to lead to, innovative classroom practice through the use of integrated literacy. With examples, the authors demonstrate successful use of themes in monolingual classrooms with bilingual pupils. Planning sheets and strategies are provided as well as a rationale for this approach to literacy. A substantial bibliography of theme topics and related literature make this a very practically-oriented book.

Laycock, Liz and Washtell, Anne *Spelling And Phonics: Key Stage One, Scottish Levels A-B* 160p. Lemington Spa: Scholastic. ISBN Pb:059053391 £11.99
This is one of the Curriculum Bank series which provides information to help teachers prepare schemes of work and contains a selection of practical activities. Sections include: the alphabet, rhyme and alliteration, syllables, graphic knowledge and a collection of photocopiable sheets. A useful resource for students and beginning teachers.

Lee, Alison *Gender, Literacy, Curriculum: Rewriting School Geography* 255p. London: Taylor and Francis. ISBN Hb. 0748402977 £39.00. ISBN Pb. 0748402985 £15.95. In the USA, Hb. $69.95. Pb. $24.95.
This book is part of a series entitled 'Critical Perspectives on Literacy and Education'. It comes out of the Australian debate around literacy which unites literacy in education with matters of ideology and discourse, knowledge and power. The writer takes as her starting point debates concerned with the implications of post structuralist and feminist theory for thinking about literacy and curriculum in schools. She examines the geography curriculum with these questions in mind, and discusses classroom dynamics in geography teaching using feminist analysis and discourse analysis. She ends by discussing the feminist politics of literacy and curriculum. Rich in the Australian perspectives on literacy, this is a demanding and intellectual book.

Lockwood, Michael *Opportunities For English In The Primary School* 176p. Stoke-On-Trent: Trentham Books, ISBN Pb. 1858560462 £9.95.
Principally aimed at student teachers and school-based mentors, this clearly presented book is set within the context of recent developments in English teaching. The book follows the National Curriculum for English in addressing speaking and listening, reading, and writing in its three main chapters. While treating these separately, the author also shows how they are integrated in practice. In addition there are shorter chapters on standard English and language study, and I.T. and media education. As well as references, specific ideas for further reading are included at the end of each chapter, and a list of addresses for computer software and

education materials is included.

Ludvig, Christine and Herschell, Paul *Talking - Our Way Into Literacy* 138p. Victoria, Australia: Curriculum Corporation. ISBN Pb. 1863662812 Australian price not available.
This volume is an outcome of a large literacy project which has produced a whole range of materials for teachers. This volume is a self-study, or group study package which explores the role of talk in literacy teaching and learning. The whole volume is very carefully constructed with examples for analysis, ideas for investigating talk and literacy, and information to help these processes. The aims of the package are: to help teachers be aware of recent research in the area; understand the relationship between talk and socio-economic status, schooling and literacy education; understand how talk constructs concepts that influence the learning and teaching of literacy; and to help teachers explore their own use of talk in literacy teaching. This is an extremely interesting and informative package.

Manzo, Anthony and Manzo, Ula *Teaching Children To Be Literate: A Reflective Approach* 595p. Orlando, Florida: Harcourt Brace College Publishers. ISBN Hb. 0153005602 $Price not available. (1995)
This American book has been written mainly for student teachers wishing to teach elementary children. It aims not just to inform but to teach, by providing a resource that can be used again and again over a period of time. The book is based on three practical assumptions: teachers should actively research finding a philosophy of teaching literacy which is right for them; teachers should make use of theory and practice to support their work; and teachers should be prepared to work in a variety of settings. The book works on the premise that literacy teachers need to be reflective practitioners throughout their careers.

Martens, Prisca *"i already know how to read": A Child's View Of Literacy* 106p. Portsmouth, New Hampshire: Heinemann. ISBN Pb. 0435072269 $18.00.
This modest book tells the story of one child's (the author's

daughter, Sarah) journey towards literacy. It is a well-written, easy -to-follow case study, which offers many insights into children's developing sense of the world of print. It is firmly linked into an 'inventive' perspective on the emergence of literacy. Included in the story is the move from home to kindergarten, where the same kind of discontinuity was experienced as the older children documented by Wells who moved from a process-centred school to a formal school (see below). The book is richly illustrated, both visually and with detailed observation. A case study such as this offers longitudinal data from one child about how literacy develops; there are a number of books which have done this, but they are relatively so few that a clear, concise, and informative addition to the genre is most welcome.

Mercer, Neil and Swan, Joan (Eds.) *Learning English: Development And Diversity* 343p. London: Routledge. ISBN Hb. 0415131219 £45.00 Pb. 0415131227 £12.99.
This is a further volume (see Maybin and Mercer above) in the series from the Open University course, *The English language: past, present and future.* The book is designed to provide a comprehensive introduction to the learning and teaching of English in diverse contexts, both as a first and a second language. The eight substantial chapters cover major topics in the learning of English, including: the acquisition of English as a first language; bilingualism; learning to read and write English; the history of English teaching; English as a classroom language; and other issues. Each chapter contains a specially commissioned study of its topic and a supplementary collection of readings. Like its companion volumes it is well illustrated and has a very accessible text.

Phinn, Gervaise *Touches Of Beauty: Teaching Poetry In The Primary School* 88p. Doncaster: Roselea Publications. ISBN Pb.0952441608 £5.00. (1995)
This small, compact and eclectic collection of poems, including many well chosen poems written by young children as well as Phinn's own, must surely invite even the most reticent or reserved to approach the teaching of poetry with excitement and sensitivity. Besides many useful explanatory notes, the reader is also offered information on a range of poetry anthologies and additional poems to those discussed in the booklet. A good resource for students or

beginning teachers.

Raphael, Taffy and Hiebert, Elfrieda *Creating An Integrated Approach To Literacy Instruction* 319p. Orlando, Florida: Harcourt Brace College Publishers. ISBN Pb. 0030515548 No price available.
This is a book which looks at the teaching of literacy in primary and middle schools. It takes as its main focus the notion of social constructivism, i.e. the child as an active learner, the importance of language in the learning process, and the fact that learning is a social process. The authors feel that in order to understand the current issues in the teaching of literacy we need to be aware of how it has developed historically and this is dealt with in the first section. The second section looks at how teachers draw upon their knowledge of the teaching of literacy to help them in their work. The third section explores practical issues which can be drawn upon to teach reading and writing; it also considers assessment procedures which may be used with literacy learners.

Routman, Regie *Literacy At The Crossroads: Crucial Talk About Reading, Writing, And Other Teaching Dilemmas* 222p. Portsmouth, New Hampshire: Heinemann. ISBN Pb. 0435072102 $19.50.
This book has been written as a response to the 'back to basics' literacy movement in the United States. Routman spends a considerable amount of the book analysing the claims of the back to basics movement and in the rest of the book explores her preferred alternatives. Those familiar with her work will understand straight away that her main concern is with literacy education that genuinely empowers children and offers them an authentic learning experience. Routman makes a strong claim that teachers who share her beliefs in the limitations and injustices of the back to basics policies need to become more overtly political in order to fight more effectively for what they believe. It is a book that should be read alongside that of Edelsky (see above).

Sampson, Michael; Sampson, Mary Beth and Van Allen, Roach *Pathways To Literacy: Process Transactions* (2nd Ed.) 578p. Orlando, Florida: Harcourt Brace College Publishers. ISBN Hb. 0155013165 No price available. (1995) The authors have added a new subtitle, "process transactions" to this the second edition of their book. They feel these two words really describe the text, as they believe that literacy learning results from the transaction between children's self expression and the impressions of the world that surrounds them. They state that the conventions of literacy are learned in the process of meaningful literacy transactions between a child and his or her world. This second edition has seven new additions which include new work on all aspects of oracy and literacy and which all contribute to make this book, "a comprehensive overview of the literacy program and a guide for teachers who wish to make literacy come alive in the hearts and minds of their students".

Sealey, Alison *Learning About Language: Issues For Primary Teachers* 138p. Buckingham: Open University Press. ISBN Pb. 0335192033 £12.99.
This book addresses the range of theoretical and practical issues which relate to the challenge posed to British primary school teachers by the requirements of the 'Standard English and language study' strand of the National Curriculum. This challenge occurs in the context of increasing interest in the questions of how young children develop metalinguistic awareness, and of how this awareness contributes to language development generally. The author's interest is in showing how these developments can be facilitated by the application of linguistics in ways which satisfy the National Curriculum requirements and through extending classroom practices in the use of different kinds of authentic spoken and written texts to teach children about language.

Shimron, Joseph (Ed.) *Literacy And Education: Essays In Memory Of Dina Feitelson* 295p. New Jersey: The Hampton Press. ISBN Hb. 1572730323 $44.95. ISBN Pb. 1572730331 $19.95. (Distributed in the UK by Eurospan Hb. £39.95. Pb.17,95)
The chapters of this book have been written by friends and fellow

researchers of Dina Feitelson. The book's twelve chapters are organised in four sections. The first four chapters review studies aimed at increasing our understanding of factors influencing the development of literacy related perceptions and skills in the years before schooling. A further set of four chapters consider learning strategies and curriculum developments aimed at promoting literacy development within the school system. The following three chapters adopt a reconciliatory approach to the debate between protagonists of whole language and basic skills. The final chapter reviews a new research study that reinforces the view that phonological knowledge is essential in reading all writing systems.

Trussell-Culen, Alan *Inside New Zealand Classrooms* 190p. Katonah, New York: Richard C. Owen Publishers Inc. ISBN Pb. 1878450425 $18.95.
The purpose of this book is to offer educators the opportunity to explore what goes on in New Zealand classrooms. This is particularly relevant to literacy educators, given the number of ways in which New Zealand research and practice has influenced practice in other countries. The book provides a fascinating account of life in five classrooms. Each portrait of a classroom claims to represent the typical experience of a single age-group, and the five examples cover ages from five to thirteen years. While the whole curriculum is observed, the main focus is on language and literacy teaching. For those who have used materials or practices developed in New Zealand this book illustrates how these practices are set in a wider curriculum and educational context.

Washtell, Anne and Laycock, Liz *Spelling And Phonics: Key Stage Two. Scottish Levels C-E* 160p. Leamington Spa: Scholastic. ISBN Pb.0590533924 £11.99.
This is one of the Curriculum Bank series which provides information to help teachers prepare schemes of work and contains a selection of practical activities. Sections include: alphabetic and dictionary knowledge, rhymes and homophones, word families, curiosities and a collection of photocopiable sheets. A useful resource for students and beginning teachers.

Webster, Alec. Beveridge, Michael and Reed, Malcolm
Managing The Literacy Curriculum: How Schools Can Become Communities Of Readers And Writers 188p. London: Routledge. ISBN Hb. 041511294-X £40.00. ISBN Pb. 041511295-8 £12.99. In the USA, Hb. $59.95. Pb. $19.95.
This is a very important contribution to the debate about standards of literacy, of interest to teachers of all age levels. The book provides a scholarly, even-handed, and critical survey of current understandings about literacy, drawing on theoretical work as well as research studies. It then moves on to establish a rationale for the project's research methodology. The authors effectively argue for a redefinition of literacy in terms of the whole curriculum. While not a new concept in itself, they present a compelling case for moving the notion of literacy on, to locate it inextricably in subject disciplines, as an intrinsic part of every subject. What is new here is a set of challenges for every school, carefully argued, rigorously researched, and set out in the context of actual classroom life.

Wells, M. Cyrene *Literacies Lost: When Students Move From A Progressive Middle School To A Traditional High School* 193p. New York: Teachers College Press. ISBN Hb. 0-807734780 $40.00. In the UK this book is distributed by Eurospan, Hb. £31.95; Pb. £15.95.
In this fascinating book Wells follows a group of students as they move from a child-centred, process-oriented middle school into a traditional high school. The difference is best encapsulated by the difference between the twenty-three page philosophy statement of the middle school, and the sixty-eight page student handbook of the high school which was almost entirely 'procedures, rules and consequences'. The chapters in the book first describe the children, their school and life in the eighth-grade classroom in the middle school and shows how literacy was a rich, intense and demanding experience. Next, chapters describe the high school, the process of becoming high school students and how the nature of the literacy demands made upon the children narrowed and diminished, and were dominated by rule-bound and exercise based tasks. Wells focuses in on a small group of children so the reader is able to get close to children's responses to these changes in their lives and in particular their beliefs, experiences and expectations about literacy.

Whitehead, Marion *The Development Of Language And Literacy* 130p London: Hodder and Stoughton. ISBN Pb. 0340644141 £9.99.
This is a very accessible book for all people involved with the education of young children, in particular their literacy development. The first chapter looks at the development of language, and this is followed by a consideration of young bilingual children and their needs and requirements. The importance of stories, narrative and play in relation to language is considered next, followed by a look at literacy teaching from birth to eight years of age. Finally, the importance of involving parents and carers in the language development of their children is given a whole section. Overall, this book is a very practical book for those involved with the education of the under-eights.

Whitmore, Kathryn and Goodman, Yetta (Eds.) *Whole Language Voices In Teacher Education* 339p. Yorke, Maine: Stenhouse Publishers. ISBN Pb. 1571100121 $35.00. Distributed in the UK by Paul Chapman Publishing £26.00.
This book, developed by hundreds of CELT members, aims to provide a framework enabling teacher educators committed to a whole language approach to teaching in the classroom situation, to use the same approach with student teachers. Many of the chapters endeavour to help whole language teacher educators in universities and colleges teach in the way they would eventually like their student teachers to teach. The authors provide much food for thought in the form of a philosophical and theoretical framework along with many usable, practical ideas. This book was written by many distinguished research professors and teacher educators and is therefore a sharing of some of the most up-to-date thinking from the United States.

Wilde, Sandra (Ed.) *Notes From A Kidwatcher: Selected Writings of Yetta M. Goodman* 316p. Portsmouth, New Hampshire: Heinemann Education. ISBN Pb 0-435088688 $24.50.
At last an anthology of Yetta Goodman's work on literacy. Chosen from over 100 published articles and book chapters, this collection focuses on work that is of historical importance, is central to Yetta Goodman's theoretical position, is not already widely available or

is of ongoing relevance to teachers. The articles have been grouped under six sections each of which is introduced by Yetta Goodman. The six sections include: 'Culture and Community'; 'Miscue Analysis'; 'Reading Strategies and Comprehension'; 'Print Awareness and the Roots of Literacy'; 'The Writing Process'; 'Kidwatching" and finally 'Whole Language'. This book, long overdue as the cover blurb states, is going to be a treat for anyone and everyone who professes a serious interest in language and literacy.

Wortman, Bob and Matlin, Myna *Leadership In Whole Language: The Principal's Role* 143p. Yorke, Maine: Stenhouse Publishers. ISBN Pb. 1571100121 $16.00. Distributed in the UK by Paul Chapman Publishing £12.99. (1995)
This book, eminently suitable for senior staff in schools, shares the work of two very successful American principals whose particular philosophy on learning and teaching is based on whole language. This has enabled them to become more effective leaders in their schools. The whole language philosophy, underpinned by a strong respect for persons, has helped Wortman and Matlin in the day-to-day running of their schools. Whole language is related to issues such as discipline, teacher appointments, parental involvement, staff development and whole school policies and are all covered in this readable and very helpful book.

Reading

Chall, Jeanne *Learning To Read: The Great Debate* (3rd Ed.) 376p. Orlando, Florida: Harcourt Brace College Publishers. ISBN Hb. 0155030809 $28.00.
When first published in 1965 'Learning to Read: The great debate' was quickly recognised as an important book. It made an invaluable contribution to the discussion of approaches to teaching reading. A second edition published in 1983 contained a new introduction. The present edition contains the original text and the previous introductions as well as a new introduction in which Chall considers theory, research and practice from 1983 to 1996. Historians will find the original text of particular interest, while the

update will add to the continuing debate. It is unlikely to solve the problem, as Chall concludes, 'It would seem the time has come to give more serious attention to why practice has been so little influenced by existing research.'

Chall, Jeanne *Stages Of Reading Development* (2nd Ed.) 296p. Orlando, Florida: Harcourt Brace College Publishers. ISBN Hb. 0155030817 £30.00.
The well-received first edition of this book (1983) on reading education is included in its entirety. Chall's work is a detailed analysis of the qualitative changes in reading from its early beginnings to its most advanced, highly skilled forms, as well as how these stages have been used in teaching and teacher education. The identification of stages is closely identified with curriculum content at specific grades. The book's foundation in a wide range of research and depth of discussion makes it undoubtedly of interest also to an audience outside the USA. The text covers the differences in development for bilinguals, the deaf, and those with learning disabilities. It also explores historical, social and cultural aspects of reading development. Chall is particularly concerned with the effect the rising average literacy level in the United States has on those who are under-achieving and the implications of this failure for policies concerned with literacy education. This edition contains a new chapter which presents theory, research and practice from 1983 to 1994 related to her developmental model of reading maturation.

Cheek, Earl., Flippo, Rona and Lindsey, Jimmy *Reading For Success In Elementary Schools* 519p. Dubuque, Iowa: Brown and Benchmark Publishers. ISBN Pb. 069727926X $40.00. In the UK, £21.95.
Those keen to brush up their knowledge about reading research and its impact on up-to-date practices will find this comprehensive volume most informative. Detailed descriptions, succinct summaries and critical evaluations are interwoven skilfully to fulfil the needs of the reader wishing to dip in to the text as well as the one who will follow its exacting interactive tasks dutifully from beginning to end. All aspects of literacy teaching are addressed in depth with definitions and explanations of their diverse histories helping the uninitiated in particular to locate essential sources and schools of

thought. The vast volume considers a wide range of readers in multicultural and bilingual American early years and elementary school settings working with different texts, especially information texts requiring study skills, literacy skills and strategies. Although principally addressing a North American readership, this book has much to offer to teachers and teacher educators in the UK.

Cooper, Margaret *Helping Children Read* 74p. Herts: United Kingdom Reading Association. ISBN Pb. 1897638124 No price available.
This brief but up-to-date account of sound support for those concerned with the teaching of reading, reviews all its aspects and ages up to the early teens. The stance adopted by the author takes seriously the disposition of the learner and the complex nature of the enterprise. The easy-to-read style makes this pamphlet an ideal text for an audience keen to develop an informed perspective of the topic.

Daniels, Harvey *Literature Circles: Voice And Choice In The Student-Centered Classroom* 200p. Yorke, Maine: Stenhouse Publishers. ISBN Pb. 1571100008 $18.50. Distributed in the UK by Paul Chapman Publishing £14.50. (1995)
"Readers love to talk, readers need to talk and readers do talk." In this interesting, exiting and innovative book, Daniels states these obvious but not always acted upon facts. The underlying premise of this wonderful book on literature circles is that children learn to read by being encouraged to read independently, by being allowed to choose what they want to read and then by being encouraged, indeed nurtured, into doing what comes naturally to people who have read a book - sharing it and talking about it in a collaborative, co-operative and supportive environment. Daniels writes about literature circles with an almost missionary zeal and it is evident that he feels they are one of the most important ways of getting children to make sense out of reading, and to talk about their reading with peers in the school situation.

Dixon, Neill., Davies, Anne and Politano, Colleen *Learning With Readers Theatre: Building Connections* 154p. Winnipeg: Peguis Publishers. ISBN Pb. 1895411807 Canadian $17.00.

This is a practical guide aimed at the classroom teacher. Its aim is to enable teachers to develop pupils' literacy skills through the use of 'Reader's Theatre' - the oral reading and performance of parts from scripts and texts of many kinds. The books includes a rationale, practical ways of starting the work with classes, as well as specific exercises designed to enhance children's textual explorations. Thus chapters are included on storytelling through scripted performance, the oral and physical interpretation of text, the writing of scripts, and rehearsing, staging, performing and evaluating the work produced. Photocopiable scripts and other resources suitable for use with classes are also included.

Edwards, Viv *Reading In Multilingual Classrooms* 28p. Reading: Reading and Language Information Centre. ISBN Pb. 0704907690 £5.95.

This slim booklet is a must for the teacher working in a multilingual setting. The author situates learning to read within the cultural and linguistic milieu of the young child which, if taken into account positively, supports the development of reading by building on a learner's existing repertoire. The well-researched text not only provides teaching suggestions, but also offers resources and assessment procedures.

Egoff, Sheila., Stubbs, Gordon; Ashley, Ralph and Sutton, Wendy *Only Connect: Readings On Children's Literature (3rd Ed.)* 416p. Oxford: Oxford University Press. ISBN Pb. 0195410246 £12.95. In the USA, $19.95.

Although there have been previous editions, this third one is to all intents and purposes a different book, since the entire selection of articles, newspaper extracts and illustrations is new. The book is organised into several sections covering important aspects of critical enquiry into children's literature: books and children; myth and folklore; fantasy; science fiction; poetry; picture books and illustration; gender relations; young adult literature, and recent trends. There are over forty pieces including several by well-known critics and authors. This is a carefully assembled and beautifully presented book which is a pleasure to handle and browse through, as well as to read more systematically. Its stimulating and eclectic content will be of interest to teachers and librarians, and to anyone studying, or with a particular interest in, children's literature.

Gambrell, Linda and Almasi, Janice (Eds.) *Lively Discussions! Fostering Engaged Reading* 316p. Newark, Delaware: International Reading Association. ISBN Pb. 0872071472 $24.95. This is a collection of eighteen chapters in which the authors use their classroom-based research and programme innovations to explore student talk about narrative and informational texts in differing classroom contexts. The authors examine student and teacher roles and offer practical and theoretical insights into classroom discussion. There are four sections: creating classroom cultures that foster discussion; discussion in action; creating the climate: the role of the teacher; and perspectives on assessing discussion. The presentation is clear and attractive, with helpful figures and quotations, and excellent sets of references at the end of each chapter to allow further enquiry. It is useful to find articles on this topic collected together so accessibly in one volume, and this is certainly a welcome addition to a growing area of interest within literacy research and practice.

Goodman, Kenneth *On Reading : A Common Sense Look At The Nature Of Language And The Science Of Reading* 152p. Portsmouth, New Hampshire: Heinemann Education. ISBN Pb. 0-435-07200-5 $20.00.
Kenneth Goodman's latest book, written in his usual easy-to-follow style, takes as a basic tenet that all of the current confusion about the teaching of reading exists because people are not sure of exactly what reading actually is, but also because people have started in the wrong place, with letters, letter-sound relationships and words. Goodman says we must begin by looking at reading in the real world and at how readers and writers try to make sense with each other. He uses examples of real children's reading and shares with teachers the strategies that children develop to enable them to try to make sense out of print. This straightforward book is suitable for teachers and interested parents and could be seen as a follow on to his earlier book, 'Phonics Phacts'.

Goodman, Yetta and Marek, Ann (Eds.) *Retrospective Miscue Analysis: Revaluing Readers and Reading* 228p. Katonah, New York: Richard C. Owen Publishers Inc. ISBN Pb. 1878450859 $24.95.

Miscue analysis is a term familiar to most teachers of reading and they will already be aware of the valuable insights such analysis can provide about the reading process in action. In this book the authors take the process forward and explore the idea of making knowledge about miscues available to the readers themselves. 'Through analysing their own reading, readers discover for themselves that reading is a process of predicting, inferring, sampling, confirming, and correcting.' Part One explores the concept of retrospective miscue analysis through discussion of its roots in socio-psycholinguistic transactional reading theory. Part Two considers research that supports its use as an instructional strategy and Part Three reports teachers' own experiences of using this technique in the classroom.

Goodman, Yetta., Watson, Dorothy and Burke, Carolyn *Reading Strategies: Focus On Comprehension* (2nd Ed.) 277p. Katonah, New York: Richard C. Owen Publishers Inc. ISBN Pb. 1878450867 $24.95.

Set within a whole language philosophy of teaching reading, this book applies socio-psycholinguistic concepts to specific reading lessons. It thus contradicts the notion that whole language does not involve teachers actually teaching. The book is in two parts. Part One places the reading process within a language framework in a sociocultural context. It gives the authors' reasons for their whole language comprehension-centred transactional reading approach. Part Two presents a series of specific strategy lessons. These are focused on the language cueing systems: semantic/pragmatic, syntactic, and graphophonic. Reading strategies of sampling, inferring, predicting, confirming and integrating meaning are also considered.

Gregory, Eve *Making Sense Of A New World: Learning To Read In A Second Language* 200p. London: Paul Chapman Publishing. ISBN Pb. 1853962635 £14.95. In the USA, Taylor and Francis $25.95.

Eve Gregory is very interested in cultural contexts and the literacy practices of young children, bilingualism and home school family literacy practices. From a cross-cultural viewpoint this book examines how educators of young, non-English speaking children can help them begin to learn a new language and therefore a new culture. Gregory's main aim is to offer general principles for good practice and at all times the book shares examples of non-English speaking children trying to make sense of a new world, both in terms of language and culture. These constant references to real children in real situations give the book an authentic "feel" in relation to the ways in which emergent bilinguals struggle to learn a new language and relate to new environments.

Harrison, Colin *The Teaching of Reading: What Teachers Need To Know* 64p. Herts: United Kingdom Reading Association. ISBN Pb. 1897638116 No price available.

The brief for this compact volume is considerable: to compile an overview of research literature relating to the teaching of reading in the first year of formal literacy instruction in school. The book very successfully explores major professional, academic and public controversies that continue to beset the teaching of reading by crystallising implications of fundamental importance for early literacy practices. The impressive spectrum of research under examination includes studies from the UK and other European countries, the USA and Canada, Australia and New Zealand.

Honig, Bill *Teaching Our Children To Read: The Role Of Skills In A Comprehensive Reading Programme* 151p. Thousand Oaks, California: Corwin Press. ISBN Hb. 0803964048 $42.95. ISBN Pb. 0803964056 $18.95. In the UK, Sage, Hb. £35.00. Pb. £15.50.

Informed by research, this North American publication advocates a systematic programme for the teaching of reading to be used alongside a literature-based approach. The case for balance in the teaching of reading is presented, together with a discussion of what skilled readers do. Specific guidance for reading instruction is offered for different age groups, from preschool to upper elementary grades. Later chapters deal with spelling, beginning writing and vocabulary, comprehension and assessment, and writing and speaking. Some frequently asked questions are addressed. Appendices summarise the role of skills in a comprehensive elementary reading programme and suggest a detailed curriculum timetable.

James, Frances *Phonological Awareness: Classroom Strategies* 27p. Herts: United Kingdom Reading Association. ISBN Pb. 1897638078 No price available.
This booklet is written by an Advisory Headteacher and is the distillation of her work in schools on developing children's phonological awareness through a range of classroom activities. Topics included are general listening skills, rhyme, alliteration, rhythm and appreciation of syllables and phonemes. Findings from relevant research are linked to practical suggestions for teachers of children entering formal education. While a short work, the practical suggestions are easily accessible for the teacher or trainee teacher.

Jones, Rhian *Emerging Patterns Of Literacy* 256p. London: Routledge. ISBN Hb.0415130492 £45.00. In the USA $69.95.
This book is a welcome addition to those studies of literacy development that are longitudinal and immensely detailed. The book is based upon the reading behaviours of two children and their parents, one the book's author. Despite the generality of its title, it focuses entirely upon reading story, and in particular the parent/child reading event. The text is divided into four sections. The first explores a number of issues relating first contact with books and the development of self. The second examines the semantics of picture-book reading. The third considers the ontogenesis of narrative and finally, a fourth section continues the exploration of self and literacy. The book is not about the teaching of reading but attempts to situate reading within a wider context of child development, a somewhat different perspective to most related books on the topic.

McClure, Amy and Kristo, Janice (Eds.) *Books That Invite Talk, Wonder, And Play* 345p. Urbana, Illinois: National Council For The Teaching Of English. ISBN Pb. 0814103707 $19.95.

This is a companion volume to NCTE's earlier publication 'Inviting children's response to literature'. Here the focus shifts from children sharing their responses to books, to writers sharing their thoughts with children. The book's fifty chapters cover an extraordinary range of topics and authors in the world of children's books. Eleven early chapters cover discrete topics including: literary genres and literary language; using non-fiction, the language of notable books. The remaining chapters are dedicated to the 'author's voices'. Here, many of today's best-known North American writers for children describe their aims and experiences in writing particular books. These reflective essays cover many different genres of children's literature, including: fantasy, folklore, picture books, non-fiction and poetry. The volume also has a very large bibliography of notable books for children.

Marantz, Sylvia and Marantz, Kenneth *The Art Of Children's Picture Book: A Selective Reference Guide* (2nd Ed.) 293p. New York: Garland Publishing Inc. ISBN Hb. 0815399376 $43.00. In the UK, £25.50. (1995)

This bibliographical guide extensively supplements the first edition by adding details of all North American publications related to children's picture books published between 1987 and 1995. The book does not claim to mention material published outside North America, a different stance from the first edition. Nor is it a guide to the picture books themselves, for which there are already many sources of information. This guide includes books and articles, essays and research studies about this form of children's literature and its practitioner authors and artists. Bibliographical references include brief descriptive synopses, and are grouped into broad categories: The history of children's picture books; The making of picture books; Criticism of picture books; Anthologies of artists; Books, articles and audio-visual material on individual artists; Guides to further research; and Collections of materials on picture books and their creators. Finally, the book provides comprehensive indexes of artists, authors and titles.

Meek, Margaret *Information And Book Learning* 128p. Stroud: Thimble Press. ISBN Pb.0903355493 £7.95

Most readers will know the works of Margaret Meek for their attention to fictional texts. In this fascinating work she turns her attention to information books. As might be expected, she brings to the topic new insights, a critical mind, and an ability to refocus perspectives on the topic. The word information is important as she rejects notions of a conventional separation into fiction and non-fiction. Non-fiction has been seen by many as requiring rather formalised strategies for coping with text, while Meek prefers to see these informational texts as generating the same uncertainty, probability, hypothesis-making and puzzling as narrative texts demand from a reader. In her special way Margaret Meek opens up new agendas for those concerned with the reading of informational texts.

Miller, Linda *Towards Reading* 134p. London: Hodder and Stoughton. ISBN Hb. 0335192165 £40.00. ISBN Pb. 0335192157 £12.99.

Despite its title, this book focuses on both reading and writing development in the pre-school years. It offers an overview of the area, covering not only reading and writing specifically, but also parental involvement, the role of the adult, observing and recording early literacy development, and provision for literacy in the pre-school. Perhaps the real strength and distinctiveness of this book lies in the extensive coverage relating to home and parental involvement, which operates in many ways and at many levels and permeates so many of the chapters (see also Weinberger later in this guide). It is clearly written, contains numerous practical suggestions and is richly illustrated with transcripts and descriptions.

Redfern, Angela *Practical Ways To Teach Phonics* 22p. Reading: Reading and Language Information Centre. ISBN Pb. 0704910624 £3.95.

This beautifully designed booklet shows the author's intent to contextualise the teaching of phonics not only in terms of the National Curriculum but also, and more importantly so, in the teaching of language as a whole. The perspective offered highlights the need for an informed approach to teaching phonics; one which translates most recent research findings into classroom practice.

Individual learning needs are explored and outlined side-by-side with a listing of points to be considered when drawing up a school policy.

Redfern, Angela *Practical Ways To Organise Reading* 22p. Reading: Reading and Language Information Centre. ISBN Pb. 0704910632 £3.95.
The beginning teacher in the British primary school especially, but not exclusively, will welcome this compact and practice-oriented summary of important management issues for teachers at both primary key stages. As the title promises, the booklet offers a range of suggestions to help unpack the multitudinous requirements for teaching reading intelligently and imaginatively.

Riley, Jeni *The Teaching Of Reading: The Development Of Literacy In The Early Years Of The School* 132p. London: Paul Chapman. ISBN Pb. 1853963070 £13.95.
This book looks at the teaching of reading in a climate where constant political pressure is placed on educationalists, where parental demands are heard more and more, and where there is educational concern about the standard of literacy and how it is taught. Jeni Riley draws on her knowledge of research and feels that an understanding of theory and the way it supports effective teaching is crucial if teaching methods used in schools are to improve. The book has five very readable chapters, starting with 'The Importance of the First Year in School' and 'The Process of Literacy' and finishing with 'The Organisation of a Learning Environment'. Riley draws upon information gained from four case studies of children in their first year in school.

Samway, Katharine and Whang, Gail *Literature Study Circles In A Multicultural Classroom* 154p. York, Maine: Stenhouse Publishers. ISBN Pb. 1571100180 $17.50. Distributed in the UK by Paul Chapman Publishing £14.50.
The authors describe the introduction of literature study circles in a fifth/sixth grade US classroom over a four-year period. The children participating were non-native English speakers and/or from low income homes, and parents were encouraged to develop their involvement and interest in reading. It is primarily a practical

book which provides help for teachers who wish to develop literature circles. It includes transcripts, examples of written responses to books and sample documents to use with children. It also includes bibliographies of a range of US multicultural authors for children and professional reading about literature study circles.

Smith, John and Elley, Warick *Learning To Read In New Zealand* 163p. Katonah, New York: Richard C. Owen Publishers Inc. ISBN Pb. 187845062X $17.95 **(1995)**
Although this is fundamentally a description and analysis of New Zealand reading programmes, this accessible book is either directly relevant to other countries, or is useful in highlighting differences. Part One offers a clear description of how children learn to read, in chronological sequence from preschool to secondary school. Part Two examines significant themes: the relevance of theory to understanding reading development; readability; assessment; Maori children learning to read; and helping children with reading difficulties, specifically through Reading Recovery and Pause, Prompt and Praise. The book is well presented, with appropriate illustrations and photographs, and includes a useful bibliography.

Sorensen, Marilou and Lehman, Barbara *Teaching With Children's Books: Paths To Literature-Based Instruction* 270p. Urbana, Illinois: National Council For The Teaching Of English. ISBN Pb.0814152929 $19.95. **(1995)**
Sensitising young children to literature is at the heart of this rich volume. The twenty-seven essays bring into focus the wide spectrum of literacy concerns shared by professionals who work with young children. The essays explore the educative dimension of literature in early literacy teaching with an insightful historic overview provided at the outset summarising the movement. Some of the texts used in the teaching suggestions are by English authors or are also available in England, thus the book is useful to educators on both sides of the Atlantic.

Spillman, Carolyn *Integrating Language Arts Through Literature In Elementary Classrooms* 203p. Phoenix, Arizona: Oryx. ISBN Pb. 089748972 $29.95. Distributed in the UK by Eurospan, £23.95.

This book is mainly a classroom guide to recommended books for genre studies, text structure studies and theme studies. Most of the literature which is recommended has been written in recent years. The book is designed to provide a framework for using literature to integrate language arts teaching. The intended audience is North American teachers, especially beginning teachers, who are not sufficiently familiar with much of what is published for children and who need additional guidance in resourcing and planning an integrated language arts and literature programme. After an initial overview of the rationale for integration of this kind, four substantial chapters cover the broad topics of genres, structures, themes and evaluation methods. Each chapter presents a review of relevant resources followed by suggested activities. Both resources and activities are offered in two clusters, one for kindergarten to second grade, the other for third to sixth grade. An extensive appendix offers advice on building a classroom library to support the kind of programmes that are advanced by the book.

Styles, Morag and Watson, Victor (Eds.) *Talking Pictures: Pictorial Texts And Young Readers* London: Hodder and Stoughton. ISBN Pb. 034064821X £12.99.
This edited book, with twelve chapters, takes as its central tenet that children are capable of sophisticated interpretations of picture books and that a large number of those texts are worthy of serious academic, aesthetic and educational scrutiny. This book has done a wonderful job of elevating the status of the picture book and it will offer revelations to many readers about the role of picture books in the education of young children. It shows clearly how sophisticated the genre really is and how children can rise to the challenge of interacting with complex pictorial texts. For an edited collection the chapters are extremely cohesive, and the whole book maintains a consistent and interesting approach.

Styles, Morag., Bearne, Eve and Watson, Victor (Eds.) *Voices Off: Texts, Contexts And Readers* 338p. London: Cassell. ISBN Hb. 0304335789 £45.00. ISBN Pb. 0304335797 £19.99.

This a companion volume to the earlier publications, 'After Alice' and 'The Prose And The Passion', edited by the same team. Like those earlier volumes, this one presents a collection of original studies on the subject of children's literature. The twenty essays cover a wide range of perspectives and issues grouped under five headings: The voices of children; Voices from the past; Classroom voices; Voices off; and Voices of authority. As these headings indicate, the major perspectives covered by the collection include: the children, the reader, the teacher, the literary historian, the wordless text, the literary authority of the narrator and the development of critical literacy. A wide diversity of expertise is represented by the contributors who include several distinguished novelists and author/illustrators, children's booksellers, academics and teachers.

Underwood, Geoffrey and Batt, Vivienne *Reading And Understanding* 244p. Oxford: Blackwells. ISBN Hb. 0631179496 £45.00. ISBN Pb. 0631179518 £13.99. In the USA, Hb. $90.00. Pb. $19.95.

This book is presented as an 'advanced text for psychology, education and linguistics students'. It offers a review of thinking in the psychology of reading, describing processes involved in making meaning from written symbols. Chapter titles provide a clear synopsis of the book: Reading as skilled information processing; Cognitive processes in word recognition; Reading development and reading difficulties; Neuropsychological studies of reading; The role of eye movements in reading; and Reading comprehension. The book focuses on the technical aspects and its well-organised index enables readers to identify areas of interest and locate them easily. Those interested in the underpinning structures of reading, and those interested in dyslexia will find this book a useful reference.

Vandergrift, Kay (Ed.) *Mosaics Of Meaning: Enhancing The Intellectual Life Of Young Adults Through Story* 474p. Maryland: Scarecrow Press. ISBN Hb 0810831104. $42.00. In the UK, available from Shelwing Ltd. £39.00.
Most of the writers in this collection are children's or young adult librarians from the United States of America. Their contributions constitute the mosaic of the book's title; a multiplicity of approaches and points of view coming together to create a picture of how young adults can and do sense their world through engagement with stories. The volume focuses largely (but not exclusively) on young female readers and the stories they read and which are written for them. The editor's contribution takes a feminist stance towards "coming of age books for girls", and in particular how such books empower (or otherwise) their young female readers. Other chapters make use of reader-response approaches to researching and developing children's reading of fiction, and two chapters from young readers chart changes in their personal reading development.

Vandergrift, Kay (Ed.) *Ways Of Knowing: Literature And The Intellectual Life Of Young Children* 416p. Maryland: Scarecrow Press. ISBN Hb. 0810830876 $39.50. In the UK, available from Shelwing Ltd. £37.55.
Distinctions that can be made between different ways of knowing the world form the underlying arena for this book's wide-ranging collection of studies of children's literature and its diverse educational uses and effects. These distinctions form the basis for a variety of standpoints from which the reader can view literature's potential to contribute to the development of 'multiple intelligences' in the child. The contributors' perspectives include classrooms, libraries, homes, universities and writers' studios. They are also variously situated socially, culturally and politically and value literature in different media, genres and formats. However, all the contributors share a belief in the multicultural, gender-fair and non-hierachical view of children's reading materials. Distinct groups of chapters explore: the contribution of literature to aesthetic growth and to cognitive growth; its ability to combat bias of different kinds; and the value of different writers, literate technologies and media.

Watson, Victor and Styles, Morag *Talking Pictures: Pictorial Texts And Young Readers* 184p. London: Hodder and Stoughton. ISBN Pb.034064821X £13.99.
This varied and stimulating collection of papers brings a range of perspectives to consideration of the distinctive qualities of pictorial texts for young children and to the notion and value of pictorial literacy. The contributors include leading authors, illustrators, researchers, and teachers or teacher educators who have developed specialist interest in this field. Contemporary pictorial texts are subjected to critical examination to reveal their rich literary and educational potentialities. The shared belief which informs the diversity of views represented in these papers is that many pictorial texts possess levels of narrative quality which not only challenge and support complex literate interactions on the part of the young child in ways which directly develop reading skills, but also carry significant implications for the extended deployment of such texts in early years classrooms.

Writing

Derewianka, Beverly *Exploring The Writing Of Genres* 47p Herts: United Kingdom Reading Association. ISBN Pb. 1897638086 No price available.
This booklet, to a large extent, goes over ground covered in Derewianka's earlier text for the Primary English Teaching Association. That book is not particularly accessible for readers in the UK so this brief overview will be a useful addition to books reflecting the current interest in helping children explore different forms of writing. The book commences by exploring how genres can be recognised, discusses genre and register and considers some genres typically found in educational contexts. Most of the booklet is devoted to a more detailed consideration of particular genres.

Edwards, Viv *Writing In Multilingual Classrooms* 28p. Reading: Reading and Language Information Centre. ISBN Pb. 0704907720 £5.95. **(1995)**
Although brief, this booklet is packed with insights and information; it is very clear and contains surprisingly detailed discussion of issues and practices associated with helping children

learning to write English as a second language. This is a relatively unexplored area, although there have been a number of books published in recent years. This account points out that most practices for such children need not be significantly different from those for native-English speaking children, but that the recognition of writing as a social process means that children from different cultures are likely to bring to instruction different ways of valuing and making sense of writing. There is a rich range of suggestions to help teachers.

Emmel, Barbara., Resch, Paula and Tenney, Deborah *Argument Revisited; Argument Redefined: Negotiating Meaning In The Composition Classroom* 230p. Thousand Oaks, California: Sage Publications. ISBN Hb. 0761901841 $48.00. ISBN Pb. 076190185X $22.95. In the UK, Hb. £38.95. Pb. £18.95.
The contributing authors and editors to the book are all North American academics concerned with teaching an argumentative approach in English composition for university students. The book is divided into two sections. In the first, recognised approaches to argument - enthymeme, evidence, classical rhetoric, Toulmian and Rogerian - are presented and discussed. In the second, movements that have included some inimical attitudes to argument - feminism, narratology and reflexive reading - are reconciled with the overall contention that argument stands up as a genre and as a process that can serve students well. The book presents a concordance that learning how to write effectively for a purpose - to persuade - entails above all learning to read critically and think inquiringly.

Goldblatt, Eli *'Round My Way': Authority And Double-Consciousness In Three Urban High School Writers* 179p. Pittsburgh: University of Pittsburgh Press. ISBN Hb. 0822938790 $49.95. ISBN Pb. 022955636 $19.95. Distributed in the UK by Eurospan. Hb. £39.95 Pb. £15.95. (1995)
In this very interesting book Goldblatt takes a detailed look at three writers from a high school for low-income students. It focuses upon writing done during one year, concentrating on journals and drafts of reports written about their neighbourhoods. What Goldblatt is

claiming is that authorship rather than being a psychological construct, is a social construct in which authors derive their authority from identification with institutions that sponsor writing. Therefore, for young learners or basic writers the struggle is to learn school (and the authority invested in the institution of schooling) rather than simply learn to write. Goldblatt offers a rich and insightful analysis of the way this influences the path of young learners towards becoming an author.

Grabe, William and Kaplan, Robert *Theory And Practice Of Writing: An Applied Linguistic Perspective* 487p. London: Longman. ISBN Pb. 0582553835 £18.99
The authors set out to provide a comprehensive view of what it means to take an applied linguistic perspective on writing. It certainly is comprehensive and detailed, and offers a view which has been rather unrepresented in recent writing about writing. The authors explore a range of issues in writing instruction, offer a model of the text construction process and discuss in some detail the nature of the writing process. They then explore the move from theory to practice and examine instruction at different levels - beginning to advanced. These chapters are centred around a number of themes for writing instruction. The authors also consider issues to do with responding to writing and assessing writing. This is a substantial book and raises a large number of significant questions that need to be addressed by those concerned with teaching writing.

Johnson, Paul *Children Making Books* 16p. Reading: The University of Reading Reading and Language Information Centre. ISBN 0 7049 0714 3. £3.95.
This slim volume introduces the rich world of Paul Johnson's wonderful book arts skills. Writing is presented as an integral part of art, design, technology and personal and social development, and is explored through many examples. The teacher wishing to replicate the ideas for the first time should find the clear instructions to the simple paper engineering and the accompanying teaching notes for writing most useful.

Johnson, Paul *Words And Images On The Page: Improving Children's Writing Through Design* 90p. London: David Fulton Publishers. ISBN Pb. 1853464430 £12.99. In the USA, Taylor and Francis, $24.95.

This is an important book. Out of many hundreds of books about children's writing it seems to be the first which seeks to help children see the written page as a designed object. As theorists talk of literacies, and analysis of texts becomes semiotic, so what a text looks like has potentially as much power as what the text says (see Goodman and Graddol - 'Redesigning English', and Kress and Van Leeuwen in this guide). In this modest-sized book Paul Johnson provides a host of ideas which could considerably improve the sensitivity of children to the appearance of their pages, books and texts. The book is very practical, copiously illustrated with examples, and has a clearly-written, straightforward text. Perhaps its greatest potential is to make teachers more aware of the relationship between design and text.

Johnson, Paul *Pictures and Word Together: Children Illustrating And Writing Their Own Books* 170p. Portsmouth: New Hampshire: Heinemann Books. ISBN Pb. 0435088831 $27.50 **(1997)**

Yet another book in which Paul Johnson seeks to stretch teachers' understanding of the rich possibilities of having children explore the world of bookmaking. In this text he focuses on the interrelationship between illustration and text. As with all his books, this one has numerous illustrations, and a well-thought out, accessible text. The book covers a range of age groups and offers a wonderful collection of practical ideas. The book takes the reader through the whole process, from story boarding, planning, illustrating, creating story characters and settings and evaluating words and pictures. What comes across so clearly in all his books is the evident enjoyment of the child authors and illustrators who have created all the work displayed in the pages.

Kress, Gunther *Before Writing: Rethinking The Paths To Literacy* 175p. London: Routledge. ISBN Pb. 0415138051 £13.99. In the USA, Hb. $65.00. Pb. $18.95.

This book develops the author's social semiotic theories of language and examines drawing and writing by young children to produce new theoretical models of children's path to literacy. Gunther Kress argues that children make texts within a multimodal setting, and read off the signs that adults give to them in terms of their own experience, or 'representational resources'. He offers a transforming account of children's meaning making in contemporary culture. The final chapters argue that we need to re-think the future, and link the design work done by children with the ever-developing visual world of computers and multimedia to produce a new curriculum for the 21st century. Stimulating for its theoretical models and readings of children's work, and useful for those working with young children.

McCracken, Marlene and McCracken, Robert *Spelling Through Phonics* (Revised second edition) 184p. Winnipeg: Peguis Publishers. ISBN Pb. 1895411866 Canadian$18.00.
This is a second edition of a book which presents learning to spell as a sensory experience incorporating visual, auditory and tactile information. It provides a background review of the demands and difficulties of the spelling process. The necessity of mastering an alphabetic system using insights into the printed word is stressed, alongside the importance of phonological awareness. Reading and writing skill development is charted sequentially from Kindergarten to Grade three (5-8 years). Information on teaching strategies and reviewing progress is presented along with word lists and dictation passages.

Sassoon, Rosemary *The Acquisition Of A Second Writing System* 160p. Oxford: Intellect. ISBN Pb. 1871516439 £14.95.
In this innovative book, Sassoon explores what it means for second language learners to acquire English literacy when the scripts of their native language differ so considerably from the Latinate English script. This has become increasingly an interesting issue in both the US and Europe as immigration from the Middle East and Far East has increased in recent years. The book introduces the reader to different writing systems, compares their rules, considers writing materials and writing posture, and examines assessment. The last few chapters are a bit of a strange mixture running from handwriting and personality, through to computers and handwriting. The book raises a fascinating and important topic and one which is clearly under-researched.

Straub, Richard and Lunsford, Ronald *Twelve Readers Reading: Responding To College Student Writing* 477p. Cresskill, New Jersey: Hampton Press. ISBN Hb. 1881303403 $28.95. Distributed in the UK by Eurospan, £23.50. **(1995)**
This substantial North American study addresses the important question of how teachers indicate their responses to the writing of their students by means of written comments. The authors report the findings of their own research in which they secured the participation of twelve eminent and experienced university specialists in writing instruction and recorded written responses to a representative sample of sixty pieces of first year college writing. This provides the data for an analysis of response strategies and the potential of commentary to provide a model from which students can learn to be effective critics of their texts. The authors display copies of assignments and commentary, develop a critical procedure for analysing responses, distinguish different response styles and also identify common strategies shared by various teachers. Many issues are raised and amongst those fully discussed are: how best to frame comments to help students; how to address error; how to respond to content; how to respond to highly personal writing; how to offer help with revision without taking authorial control, and how to relate comments to students' long-term growth as writers.

Wolf, Denise and Craven, Julie *More Than The Truth: Teaching Nonfiction Writing Through Journalism* 134p. Portsmouth, New Hampshire: Heinemann Books. ISBN Pb. 0435072161 $19.50.
More Than The Truth is the first of four volumes recording the 'Curriculum Seminars', an innovative two-year professional development experience for urban middle school teachers in different parts of America. This volume tells the story of the first seminar - an immersion in the craft of journalism, with all of its demands to observe, use primary sources, and make ideas come alive while remaining honest and fair. An interesting part of the account is how the teachers, before setting out to teach, themselves became students, immersing themselves in the unfamiliar world of professional journalism as novice writers. The book reveals students and teachers engaged in real conversations about literacy made all

the more powerful by inquiry and debate.

Special needs

Attwood, P. and Attwood, T. *The Multi-Sensory Approach To Literacy Skills* (Unpaged) Oundle, Peterborough. ISBN: Pb. 1860830463 £10.95 **(1995)**
This set of partly photocopiable materials provides an overview of the components of multi-sensory techniques and simple guidelines on implementation. It is linked to, and derives from, the "Multi-sensory Learning Course". From an opening definition of the multi-sensory approach and a brief review of history and development, the book describes the elements of a multi-sensory session. One section compares these with Reading Recovery techniques. Resources for further study are suggested.

Barbieri, Maureen and Tateishi, Carol *Meeting The Challenges: Stories From Today's Classrooms* 152p. Portsmouth, New Hampshire: Heinemann Books. ISBN Pb. 0435072250 $24.00.
In this book the authors share accounts they have collected which relate to struggling readers. Not all of the accounts are success stories, but every one is candid, thought provoking, and moving. These teachers know their students well; they strive to develop classroom cultures that nurture self-worth, engagement, and passionate curiosity. While the contexts vary widely, the teachers have several common values: high expectations, a belief in the necessity of a classroom community, and a willingness to adapt their personal styles to meet the needs of their particular students. These teachers choose to work from personal philosophies that take both traditional and progressive techniques into consideration.

Broomfield, Hilary and Combley, Margaret *Overcoming Dyslexia: A Practical Handbook For The Classroom* 226p. London: Whurr Publishers Ltd. ISBN Pb. 1861560087 £19.50. Available in the USA from Singular Publishing Group, no price available
Written by two teachers, drawing on their experience of language and literacy difficulties, this book offers a thorough and practical

approach for teachers, speech therapists and educational psychologists to follow with pupils not only with dyslexic difficulties but also speech and language disorders and more general learning difficulties. The first part of the book gives the research background for the teaching approach suggested making use of illustrative case studies from the authors' own experiences. The second section, 'Skills into action' looks at using this knowledge in the classroom, closely relating suggestions to the demands of current legislation on special educational needs. The final section provides a thorough guide to introducing sound/letter links, and includes relevant worksheets and games.

Davis, Ronald *The Gift Of Dyslexia* 226p. London: Souvenir Press. ISBN: Pb. 0285632817 £9.99 In the USA, published by Ability Workshop Press at $14.95. (1995)
This book, designed to be read by teachers, psychologists and parents of dyslexic children, attempts to give a new understanding about what dyslexia is and what it means to be dyslexic. Four sections detail what dyslexia is (in terms of visual processing disorientation), give a developmental theory of dyslexia through a 'case study' of a potential dyslexic, describe the talents shared by dyslexic people, and finally make recommendations for identifying and helping people with the 'dyslexic gift'. Dyslexia is seen as a reliance on non- verbal perception, as a gift rather than a disability. While the book is highly positive and novel in looking at dyslexia as a gift rather than a disabling condition its impact may be lessened by the lack of research offered to justify the book's claims.

Doyle,J. *Dyslexia: An Introductory Guide* 218p. London: Whurr. ISBN Pb. 1897635672 ££14.95. In the USA it is published by Singular Press at $39.95.
This well-researched and detailed book provides an overview of the field of dyslexia. The intended audience is concerned parents or teachers of dyslexic children. The book describes the measurement of reading and provides an overview of the aetiology of reading difficulties. The influence of intelligence and mental age is discussed. A comprehensive chapter examines the theoretical background with reference to problems of terminology, definition and the importance of sub-type theory. The issue of causation is addressed in two chapters describing the respective contributions of

the brain and vision, and phonological processing. Later chapters deal with an overview of current methods of help available and advice for parents. A list of contact/information addresses and a glossary of terms are included.

French, Joyce., Ellsworth, Nancy and Amoruso, Marie *Reading And learning Disabilities* 442p. New York: Garland Publishing Inc. ISBN Hb. 0824047907 $65.00 **(1995)** This book has two sections, one a text dealing with questions and issues relating to enabling students with learning disabilities to acquire literacy skills, and the other a well-annotated bibliography of current references on this topic. The text focuses on the characteristics of students with learning disabilities and their performance in schools, compares the 'good reader' and students with learning difficulties, and examines various instructional strategies and alternatives available to teachers of learning-disabled pupils. The book is primarily intended for qualified (and trainee) teachers but would also be of use to administrators involved in special education needs policy intervention.

Heaton, Pat and Winterson, Patrick *Dealing With Dyslexia* **(2nd Ed.)** 248p. London: Whurr Publishers. ISBN: Pb. 1897635575 £16.50. In the USA it is published by Singular Press at $39.95. This is the second edition of a book first published in 1987. The most notable change is a vast improvement in presentation and layout. This edition follows exactly the same format as the first but has been updated in the light of new research. The bibliography of works consulted for this edition is actually given separately. A fairly lengthy introduction describes developments in research, most notably a shift to recognising the importance of linguistics and phonological awareness. The book is actually 3 books in one. The first is, 'About Dyslexia', the second, 'Immediate problems and strategies', and the third, 'Information: reading and the English writing system'. There is a large bibliography, a copy of the BDA Diploma reading list along with useful addresses and a very convenient chart of the 44 'significant sound units' of English.

Hornsby, Beve *Overcoming Dyslexia: A Straightforward Guide For Families and Teachers* (Rev. Ed.) 183p. London: Vermillion. ISBN: Pb. 0-091813204 £8.99. (1995)
This is a revised edition of what has been an invaluable resource for
the parents and teachers of dyslexic children since 1984. The book is a comprehensive guide to the topic, beginning with chapters on understanding and identifying dyslexia. Successive chapters focus on how parents and teachers can help children, and how a professional diagnosis can be obtained and interpreted. Specialist teaching approaches are outlined, and specific and practical suggestions for coping with dyslexia are proposed. The final two chapters deal with dyslexia and the educational law, and dyslexia and the brain. This book remains an important book about dyslexia.

McCallion, Paul *Reading: What To Teach And How To Teach It* 78p. Belfast: PMG Publications. ISBN: Pb. 1900154005 No price available (1994)
This booklet aims to provide an overview of the learning-to-read process. It relates to all levels of reading skill, from those experiencing difficulty in reading acquisition to those making faster progress than expected. The approach is intended to be used alongside
other approaches and stresses the importance of flexibility. The manual aims to inform assessment of reading, selection of goals for teaching, presentation of a range of teaching approaches, and selection of resources and guidelines for review and change of programmes.

Miles, T. and Gilroy, D. *Dyslexia At College* (2nd Edition) 259p. London: Routledge. ISBN Pb. 0415127785 £12.99.
This book offers a comprehensive overview, in short easily accessible chapters that can be read independently, of all aspects of college life that may present a problem to students with Dyslexia. Published 10 years after the first edition, the book has been updated in light of the increasing numbers of dyslexics proceeding to further education, and the trend to view dyslexia in terms of strengths as well as weaknesses. The major changes involve, (alongside a general modification to take account of experience the

authors have gained) an update of the research information, a new chapter about assessment, a wider discussion of different routes into higher education, sections on statistics, mathematics and information technology, and the move towards special examination provision being made available.

Rhodes, Lynn and Dudley-Marling, Curt *Readers And Writers With A Difference:A Holistic Approach To Teaching Struggling Readers And Writers* (2nd Ed.) 381p. Portsmouth, New Hampshire: Heinemann Books. ISBN Pb. 0435072153 $32.50.
In this second edition the authors renew the case for the role of whole language theory when working with children who experience difficulties in language and literacy. It takes into account the various developments in language arts over the past eight years. Included are new and expanded sections on literacy theory, instruction and assessment, and literacy as social practice, as well as a reconsideration of how teachers, administrators, and parents might work and learn collaboratively.

Riddick, Barbara *Living with Dyslexia* 232p London: Routledge. ISBN Pb. 0-415-12501-4 £13.99. In the USA, $18.95
This book provides an overview of the effects of living with dyslexia on a day-to-day basis. It begins with a brief overview of dyslexia, focusing on the difficulties encountered in defining it, and the rationale for looking at it from an educational perspective. The bulk of the book, however, reports on a study of 22 children that aimed to: examine the processes by which children are identified and labelled as dyslexic; explore how living with dyslexia appears from the individual perspective of children and their parents; and to consider the social and emotional consequences of having dyslexia. Each chapter concludes with suggestions for further reading and there is a list of useful addresses at the end of the book.

Roller, Cathy *Variability Not Disability: Struggling Readers In A Workshop Classroom* 160p. Newark, Delaware: International Reading Association. ISBN Pb.0872071421 $21.95

This book describes the author's experiences working with 'reading disabled' children at the University of Iowa Summer Reading Program. The program is for children of mixed ages (8-12) and reading abilities and operates as a 'workshop classroom' that takes a 'whole language' approach to reading and writing. Practical advice is given on how to set up a workshop classroom and the information given reflects both the authors' personal experience and research supporting this form of instruction. The place of direct instruction, the importance of writing in the teaching of reading and practical advice on record keeping are also given space. The book is designed to be read by mainstream classroom teachers as well as reading specialists, special education teachers and others involved with struggling readers and writers.

Snowling, Margaret and Stackhouse, Joy *Dyslexia: Speech And Language* 267p. London: Whurr Publishers. ISBN: Pb. 1897635486 £19.50. In the USA it is published by Singular press at $52.95.

This book is a collection of papers, including experimental studies, recommendations for teachers and overviews of research, that look at the link between spoken and written language difficulties. It is designed for people working in the field of children's language and learning difficulties but provides a useful overview for anyone interested in the topic. The first two chapters provide the reader with background knowledge about dyslexia, the theory behind the concept and a discussion of who is likely to be at risk of language difficulties and why. The next section of the book deals with the problems encountered in assessing language difficulties, while the final section addresses ways to intervene to help children overcome their difficulties. The full references are complimented by a list of assessment tests.

Cooper, Cathie H. *ABC Books And Activities: From Preschool To High School* 155p. Lanham, Maryland:The Scarecrow Press. ISBN Pb. 0810830132 $27.50. In the UK, £26.15.

As part of the School Library Media Series this book is initially intended for school librarians. Because of the content and because in the UK most librarians in school are most likely to be teachers, the book will have wider appeal. It is an in depth analysis of alphabet books ranging from simple instructional ABC books through various degrees of complexity to ones suited for much older children. The book is divided into sections. After an initial introduction which considers the history, the criteria for selection, and the value and use of alphabet books, a selection of books are examined under different topic headings including: first encounters, alphabet books for babies, and moving on to animals, rhyme and reason, multiculturalism, science,social studies and many more. Each section consists of descriptions of particular books followed by more general activities related to the topic and to explorations of the alphabet.

Sheridan, Jean (Ed.) *Writing-Across-The-Curriculum And The Academic Library: A Guide For Librarians, Instructors, And Writing Program Directors* 240p. Westport, Connecticut: Greenwood Press. ISBN Hb. 0313291349 $69.50, This book is distributed in the UK by Eurospan, Hb. £55.50. **(1995)**

According to the editor, writing-across-the-curriculum is a North American university pedagogic reform dating from the 1970s whereby the teaching of students' writing skills was removed from composition classes and returned to subject disciplines. Library inductions and bibliographic instruction remained the preserve of librarians. This book, which contains detailed case studies, includes reflections on the writing-across-the-curriculum movement but most centrally argues for proactive alliances between librarians and instructors of writing. Each should be motivated towards improving not simply students' research skills but their capacities for reflection as foundations for improved writing.

Senator, Rochelle *Collaborations For Literacy: Creating An Integrated Language Arts Program For Middle Schools* 168p. Westport, Connecticut: Greenwood Press. ISBN Hb. 0313291322 $35.00. Distributed in the UK by Eurospan, Hb. £27.95. **(1995)**
Coherence of interdisciplinary learning in language arts programmes and collaboration between contributing specialists are the themes of this book. Senator offers a comprehensive innovative structure of integrated language arts, progressing from vision, through planning, implementation and assessment to evaluation. The success of the programme is made to depend upon quality collaboration between the language arts teacher and the school library and media specialist. The imperative is for the collaboration to operate at every stage in the development of the programme and its assessment. She includes specific instructional programmes, suggestions for staff development, sample units for use with grades six, seven and eight, and methods of working together to develop materials for the taught programmes.

Assessment

Karavais, Sylvia and Davies, Pat *Progress In English* 32p. Reading:The University of Reading Reading and Language Information Centre. ISBN 070491060 8. £10.95??
This is an indispensable guide for the primary teacher and the primary school staff as a whole whose overriding concern when assessing achievement in English must be to have access to intelligently designed records. Devised for all modes of language and patterned on the currently operating British programs-of-study framework for English, these records support the teacher in identifying significant learning events. They demonstrate with clarity, and through examples, how the holy trinity of diagnostic, formative and summative assessment can be realised with skilfully collected and collated records.

Various *Standards For The English Language Arts* 132p.
Urbana, Illinois: National Council of Teachers of English; and
Newark, Delaware: International Reading Association. ISBN
Pb. 0814146767 $18.00.
This book is the end product of a long, and sometimes chequered,
process of developing standards for English language arts education
in the United States. It is in most respects the equivalent of the Cox
Committee report in the UK except that this report has been
produced by teacher organisations rather than a government
committee (US government funding for the project was discontinued
half way through). The book has three major sections. The first
reviews the issues surrounding the need for the development of
standards. The second explores the nature of the understanding
about language and literacy that has informed the development of
the standards. The third is the standards themselves set out grade
by grade. Some flesh is put on these bones by the addition of some
vignettes. British educators who in the light of subsequent events
have probably forgotten what an enlightened document the Cox
committee report was, will look in envy at the good sense in this
document. Whether or not it actually influences future educational
policy in the USA remains to be seen.

Adult literacy

Athreya, Venkatesh and Chunkath, Sheena *Literacy And
Empowerment* 299p. Thousand Oaks, CA: Sage
Publications. ISBN Hb. 0803993366 $38.00. In the UK, Hb.
£35.00.
This book contains an analysis of a one-year literacy campaign in
Pudukkotai, India. The campaign studied was part of India's mass
literacy programme. The book is divided into three major sections.
In the first four chapters the authors track the development of mass
literacy movements in the modern world, paying particular
attention to policies and practices within India. The following eight
chapters provided a very detailed, descriptive account of one
particular literacy campaign. The final two chapters reflect upon
that campaign and in the light of that critically review recent
developments within India's mass literacy movement. The book is
very rich in detail. is extremely honest about the successes and

failures, and is revealing about the practical difficulties in mounting educational programmes in rural communities.

Family literacy

Hydrick, Janie *Parent's Guide To Literacy For The 21st Century: Pre-K Through Grade 5* 97p. Urbana, Illinois: National Council For The Teaching Of English. ISBN Pb. 0814146880 $11.95.
Providing clear, straightforward explanations and illustrations within home and school contexts, this American book for parents covers many key concepts in literacy development and education. The book includes chapters on basic issues (basic skills, co-operative learning, authentic assessment, multi-age grouping and multiculturalism), language (including bilingualism), reading (including media literacy), writing, and a chapter on wider topics (literature across disciplines, integrated language arts, thematic units and family literacy). The book is well set out and accessible, with attractive illustrations, making it easy to browse through to find topics of interest. Throughout there are specific suggestions of ways in which parents can increase their involvement in aspects of their children's literacy development.

Rasinski, Timothy (Ed.) *Parents And Teachers: Helping Children To Read And Write* 209p. Orlando, Florida: Harcourt Brace College Publishers. ISBN Hb. 0155013157 No price available. **(1995)**
This book asks why the American education system has not done more to use parents in helping with children's education when research has consistently shown that parental involvement is crucial if positive results are to be gained. The book aims to show how parents and teachers can help children's literacy development by working together as a team and goes on to offer positive suggestions which parents can use with their children and which teachers can use as the basis for parental workshops on home literacy development.

Schiavone, James *Help Your Child To Read Better* 121p. Chicago: Nelson-Hall. ISBN Hb. Hb. 0882292218 $26.95. Distributed in the UK by Gazelle Book Services Ltd. Hb. 0882292218 £20.99.

The aim of this American book is to help parents understand the reading process, so they can work alongside teachers to help their children. The book spans the school age range, from elementary school through to adolescents in secondary school. Schiavone describes the reading process from a psychological point of view, including problems with reading, and advocates an approach to teaching using a combination of methods. There are suggestions for parents of games and experiences to help their child's reading development. Each chapter includes answers to common questions parents ask about children's reading problems. Included is a list of books (American publications) for parents and children.

Voss, Margaret *Hidden Literacies: Children Learning At Home And School* 220p. Portsmouth, New Hampshire: Heinemann Books. ISBN Pb. 0435088904 $23.50.

This book addresses three areas of significant current interest. Firstly, it goes straight to the heart of recent interest in home-school relationships but innovatively does so beyond the preschool years. Secondly, it explore what is one of the most under-researched areas in the whole field of literacy - the use made by children of literacy in their lives out of school; the richness and variety of which are seldom known by the school. Thus the title 'hidden literacies' is a very accurate representation of the book's subject matter. Thirdly it moves beyond exploring just print literacy and, in keeping with recent work in the field, explores the child's world as one featuring multiple literacies. Voss looks in great detail at some fourth-grade children as they move across the worlds of home and school, and in the process She poses many fascinating, intriguing, and important questions about the relationships between children's lives beyond schooling, and the ability of schools to tap into that major area of children's experience.

Weinberger, Jo *Literacy Goes To School: The Parents' Role In Young Children's Literacy Learning* 164p. London: Paul Chapman Publishing. ISBN: Pb. 1853962929 £13.95. Distributed in the USA by Taylor and Francis, $24.95.
This easy-to-read book looks closely at the notion of early literacy learning and how it can be nurtured in the home environment. Weinberger looks at more than 40 parents from different backgrounds and considers the effect of their contributions to the literacy development of their children. She proposes that when literacy learning takes place in the home situation, then the child's literacy performance in school can be directly enhanced. She looks at particular home-school relations and makes suggestions which will help both parents and teachers foster these kinds of positive links. She include a Home-School Evaluation matrix which helps teachers to promote and monitor change along with reviewing their contact with parents. This book is valuable addition to the literature on home-school relationships.

Wienstein-Shr, Gail and Quintero, Elizabeth (Eds.) *Immigrant Learners And Their Families: Literacy To Connect The Generations* 164p. Illinois: Delta Systems Co. Inc. (in association with Center For Applied Linguistics). ISBN: Pb. 0937354848 $13.50. (1995)
This book contains eleven chapters detailing a number of intergenerational literacy programmes directed primarily at immigrant families. In the first section, 'Programme design: focus on collaboration', the chapters explore the development of programmes that do not impose a model of learning upon the families but develop relationships which lead to collaboration in the determination of learner's needs and responsive practices. In the second section, 'Curriculum: drawing on learner strengths' the chapters focus on the nature of curriculum which uses the knowledge, experience and abilities of the learners. The third section, 'Where we are, where we are going', examines a range of issues to do with purpose and direction. This bare description does not do justice to the richness and interest in these chapters, and this book is a very welcome addition to the literature on the topic.

Yates, Irene *Writing Skills For Parents* 108p. London:
Piccadilly Press. ISBN Pb. 1853404101 £5.99
Covering many key aspects of children's writing skill development,
with practical ideas for how parents can help their children, this is
a short, accessibly presented book. The emphasis is on writing as a
developmental process, with parents encouraged to look at what
this means from the child's point of view. Stages of writing are
described, and some of the difficulties children encounter with
writing outlined, alongside suggestions for how parents can help.
There is a chapter on the rules of writing (grammar, punctuation,
spelling and handwriting) and one on the many different kinds of
writing that children do in schools. Information about the National
Curriculum, including Attainment Targets for writing at Key Stage
One and Two is included.

Video packages

Getting Better at Successful Intervention: K-3 Literacy (50
minute video and book, 228p.) Victoria: Australia: Curriculum
Corporation. ISBN Pb. 1863662790 Australian$39.00. Video
A$39.00 (PAL Format)
This package explores how a whole school policy may be developed
for literacy which allows children from different cultural
backgrounds, and of different ability to progress within mainstream
groups. The video offers demonstrations of different aspects of this
process, showing teacher planning, intervention with children and
working with parents. The book offers a comprehensive overview
of the issues, provides background information, and illustrates a
range of teaching strategies including diagnosis, classroom
management, learning about text types, instructional strategies and
many others. The book is very practical and gives detailed advice
on activities, topics, and strategies.

Viewing For Learning (Video and book, 32p.) Victoria:
Australia: Curriculum Corporation. ISBN Pb and Video
1863662774 A$45.00 (1995) (PAL Format)
This package, while about viewing, has so much in it that is related
to language and literacy, that it deserves a place in this volume. It
is primarily a video package, the brief booklet offering only an

overview of the principal points, and it provides a close look at how children can be helped to examine and unpack images as pieces of text. Indeed, in some ways it offers better advice than is sometimes available to help children critically examine written texts. The package makes it clear that (a) teachers need have no fear about helping their children understand moving and still images; what is seen on the video reflects what has always been seen as good practice, and (b) that both in principle and in practice literacy skills are ever-present in the work that is carried out by the children.

Literacy Intervention With Parents - A Framework For Practice REAL Project. Sheffield University Television. (PAL Format) £25.95
This twenty minute video is designed for teachers and other early childhood educators who wish to develop work with parents to promote early literacy. The video shows how children learn about literacy within the family and shows how schools and nursery centres can work with parents in promoting literacy development. The programme is based upon four main aspects: Opportunities for learning literacy, Recognition, Interaction and Providing a model (known as the ORIM framework). The video is brief yet concise, is extremely clear, has very good examples and explanations, and is well suited for its target audience. There are no written materials with the video; it is fully self-explanatory.